FALLOUT

A Study of Superbombs,
Strontium 90, and Survival

The Authors

JOHN M. FOWLER, assistant professor of physics, Washington University.

LESTER MACHTA, chief, Special Projects Section, United States Weather Bureau.

ROBERT J. LIST, meteorologist, United States Weather Bureau.

W. O. CASTER, assistant professor of physiological chemistry, University of Minnesota Medical School.

WALTER R. GUILD, assistant professor of biophysics, Yale University.

JAMES F. CROW, professor of genetics, University of Wisconsin School of Medicine; president, Genetics Society of America.

GOULD A. ANDREWS, associate chairman of the Medical Division, Oak Ridge Institute of Nuclear Studies.

JACK SCHUBERT, senior chemist, Argonne National Laboratory.

CHET HOLIFIELD, Representative in the United States Congress from California; chairman, Subcommittee on Military Operations and Special Subcommittee on Radiation.

ARTHUR H. ROSENFELD, assistant professor of physics, department of physics and the Radiation Laboratory, University of California.

RALPH E. LAPP, physicist and author, former assistant director of Argonne National Laboratory, executive director of Atomic Energy for Research and Development Board, and head of Nuclear Physics Branch of Office of Naval Research.

FALLOUT

A STUDY OF SUPERBOMBS
STRONTIUM 90 AND SURVIVAL

edited by
John M. Fowler

Basic Books, Inc., NEW YORK

First printing 1960
Second printing 1960
Third printing 1961

© 1960 by Basic Books, Inc.
Library of Congress Catalog Card Number: 60–7808
Manufactured in the United States of America

TO *Ada and Margaret*

Editor's Acknowledgment

In the preparation of this book I was sustained and carried forward by encouragement and assistance from many sources.

The major credit for any contribution this book makes to public understanding must go to the authors of the separate chapters; their patience, punctuality, and scholarly competence eased the load on the editor. In particular, I must thank Ralph Lapp and James Crow for help above and beyond an author's duty.

I also received much help from Leon Svirsky, Science Editor of Basic Books, Inc.; his experienced advice must be credited in any success we may achieve in presenting a difficult technical subject to a nontechnical audience.

I am deeply indebted to my colleagues, Professor Edward D. Lambe of the Department of Physics and Dr. Walter C. Bauer of The School of Medicine of Washington University, for critical reading and advice at several stages of the manuscript's preparation.

I wish to acknowledge gratefully the contribution Governor Stevenson made in taking the time from his crowded schedule to write the foreword and encourage us in this activity.

To Yasushi Nishiwaki, Professor of Radiation Protection at the Tokyo Institute of Technology, I am indebted for the Japanese data quoted in the text and for informative discussions of the fallout problems in Japan.

I must also thank Antoinette Pirie, editor of the English book *Fallout,* for her advice, stimulation, and assistance.

The tremendous accumulation of words which necessarily precedes the completion of such a book was typed by my wife Margaret. Without her secretarial help and, more important, without the faith she had in the usefulness of this effort, I could not have subtracted time from the already small allotment an academician gives his family in order to undertake the book.

Finally I must acknowledge the encouragement received from the many groups and individuals in St. Louis and elsewhere who by their intelligent interest in the problems of bombs and fallout have sustained the belief that communication between scientists and laymen is both possible and essential in our democracy.

JOHN M. FOWLER

January 17, 1960
St. Louis, Missouri

Foreword

This is not a book merely about fallout. It is a book about our nuclear quandary—about the circumstances that make our period the most uneasy in the history of mankind. On the surface there are few obvious signs of the underlying disquietude, as we enter a new decade already euphorically named "the Soaring Sixties." Industry and trade are humming; the cruise ships are filled; sports cars, the stock market, and "payola" are the popular topics of conversation; never have so many people been engaged so single-mindedly in the pursuit of creature comfort. And yet this vast spending spree still looks suspiciously like a nervous flight from perplexing realities.

Some of the realities of the Atomic Age are set forth in this book. They are spelled out in language plain enough for anyone to understand: even a layman begins to feel more at home— or less uncomfortably ignorant—on subjects which have seemed remote and mysterious. The scientists who have written it give us a rather detailed and clear picture of the anatomy of nuclear bombs and how they work; they clarify the peculiarities of radiation and the kinds of damage that fallout may be sowing in our environment, ourselves and our children; they describe in factual but vivid terms what a nuclear war would be like; and they explain what the issues are in the stalemated negotiations on the banning of bomb tests and nuclear disarmament.

Delay is dangerous. We cannot afford to let the negotiations drag. So long as the nuclear weapons race continues, more and more nations will seek prestige and influence by making their own atomic bombs. And as the list of nations armed with super-bombs grows, the chances of avoiding a nuclear catastrophe will become less and less. The outcome of the present negotiations on bomb testing by the United States, Britain and the Soviet Union may truly be a turning point in history.

ADLAI E. STEVENSON

January 28, 1960

Contents

FALLOUT

A Study of Superbombs,
Strontium 90, and Survival

JOHN M. FOWLER

Introduction

"All men should strive to know before they die what they are
running from, and to, and why."

James Thurber's moral from the tale of the lemmings and their
confused dash into the sea seems singularly appropriate for
atom-age man. The great advances we have made in weapons
technology, coupled to the unchanging myopia of our several
national visions, are accelerating us down the lemmings' path.
If we are to stop short of nuclear annihilation, fear's closed eye
and apathy's glazed eye must be cleared by knowledge.

The destruction of Hiroshima and Nagasaki previewed a
change in the nature of war. The radioactive ashes that fell on
the *Lucky Dragon* and the Marshall Islanders early in 1954
underlined the magnitude of this change. Radiological weapons
can now make entire countries the targets and continents the
battlegrounds. But with this change in the size of wars has come
no parallel growth in the statesmanship of nations. No improvement in international politics comparable to that made in
weapons has appeared. Atomic and hydrogen bombs are, it
seems, but bigger guns to the men who use them.

We shall be confronted more and more with issues vitally affecting mankind's chances of survival. Already we see the shape
they will take: the policy of deterrence with its commitment to
nuclear weapons, the building of "hardened" (H-bomb proof)

missile bases in the American heartland, the controversy over the testing of nuclear weapons—these are immediate examples. In spite of their import for our future, the decisions of governments on these matters are not being formed and guided by public opinion. Apparently the difficult and subtle nature of nuclear problems turns most laymen away, and the distortions of public discussion have left those who have tried to understand in confusion and despair.

This book is an attempt to give a clearer picture of these nuclear problems. We have attempted to present simply and authoritatively the facts about nuclear weapons and the threats they raise to mankind. We have taken the hazard of radioactive fallout as our main theme. There are three reasons for focusing on this aspect of the nuclear danger. First, the public debate of the weapons testing issue has centered on the fallout hazard, and much confusion has resulted from the incomplete and contradictory arguments presented. Secondly, intensive scientific studies in the last three or four years have produced a wealth of factual material which should be transmitted to the public. Third, any estimates of the biological effects of a nuclear war are in the last analysis largely drawn from present studies of the fallout from bomb tests.

The magnitude of this fallout hazard has been the main subject of political and scientific debate, and we shall examine the principal elements of the controversy in later chapters. It is well to start, however, by realizing just what is in dispute and what is not.

The explosion of a nuclear weapon produces radioactive debris which is carried on the winds to all parts of the world; it falls with the rain and enters the food cycles of plants and animals. That there has been a steady increase of radioactivity in our soil is not questioned; it can be and has been clearly demonstrated in many experiments, well exemplified by one performed by soil scientists at Earlham College in Indiana. In 1950, as part of a long-range study, a sample of topsoil was carefully set aside. In mid-1959 a second sample was taken from the same place.

The radioactivity of both samples was carefully measured, and it was found that the radioactivity in the top layer of the 1959 sample was more than 100 times greater than that in the 1950 sample, while below two inches the two samples showed about the same radioactivity. At the Los Alamos Scientific Laboratory similar dramatic evidence is available. A radiation detector large enough to enclose a man has been in use there for some time to measure gamma radiation from the body. The records on visitors tested with this instrument show that in the years since the testing of hydrogen bombs began there has been a gradual increase in people's accumulation of cesium 137, a radioelement formed by the nuclear bombs. Still further evidence has been accumulated over the last few years at the Lamont Geophysical Laboratory in Palisades, New York, where human bones collected from various parts of the world have been analyzed for radioactivity. The unmistakable evidence from these analyses is that there is radioactive material in our bones and that this contamination is increasing.

In milk, in wheat, in tea, in lettuce, in rice—in every foodstuff exposed to sun and rain, we find a growing concentration of radioactive material.

That the air also is loaded with radioactive material was conclusively demonstrated in the spring of 1959 when the coveralls of five mechanics who had worked on a Pan American World Airways jetliner were found to be radioactive. Subsequent investigation showed that the plane had picked up radioactive debris in easily detectable amounts on its oily surfaces during its flight through the stratosphere.

In these facts there is no basis for controversy. The evidence of a growing radioactive contamination has been obtained from simple measurement and analysis. Nor is there any question as to the source of this contamination. The materials responsible for the increased radioactivity in our surroundings, and in ourselves, can be clearly identified as fission products. The main radioactive elements in our bodies are cesium 137 and strontium 90. The air and soil activity comes from radioactive varieties of barium, lanthanum, neodymium, ruthenium, and many other unfamiliar isotopes formed from the fissioned uranium atom.

There is no controversy, either, about the general consequences of exposure to radiation. We know that in large doses nuclear radiation is lethal, and that in somewhat smaller doses it can produce leukemia and bone cancer. We know also that radiation damages genes, the material of heredity.

The disagreement among scientists begins when we try to assess the effects of our exposure to the very low levels of radiation from fallout. With little clear-cut experimental evidence to guide us, estimates depend strongly on the investigator's assumptions about the uncertain factors.

That there has been a difference in the estimate of the danger from this build-up of fission products in our environment can best be demonstrated by quoting a few statements from leading scientific figures on each side of the controversy.

Outstanding among those who have warned of the danger is Linus Pauling, 1952 Nobel Laureate and distinguished American chemist. Pauling, in his book *No More War,* makes this statement:

> A single large superbomb, like the one which was detonated by the United States on 1 March 1954, causes an incidence of disease such as to lead to the death of 10,000 people by leukemia and bone cancer and possibly also 90,000 more by other diseases, a possible total of 100,000 deaths.

In sharp contrast, Edward Teller, one of the builders of the hydrogen bomb, declares in his book, *Our Nuclear Future:*

> The reader will see that the world-wide fallout is as dangerous as being an ounce overweight or smoking one cigarette every two months.

The difference between these two statements is not as great as may appear at first glance. In a world population of 2,500,-000,000, Pauling's figure of 100,000 deaths is an almost insignificant fraction. When expressed as a percentage, fallout deaths do seem one of the minor miseries of mankind. But Teller's comparison overlooks the difference between a deliberate exposure to smoking and the involuntary and inescapable exposure to fallout radiation. This particular comparison suffers also from incorrect assumptions as to the magnitude of the fallout exposure.

How is it that two scientists can draw such divergent conclusions from the same data? Experimental measurements of the effects of continued low-level exposure are scarce, and those experiments that have been reported are generally uncertain enough to leave wide room for differences in interpretation. The two men were influenced in their interpretations by their sharply differing views on testing of nuclear bombs. Teller, believing strongly that leadership in nuclear weapons is the paramount requirement for the nation's safety, used the most optimistic estimates on the effects of fallout and emphasized the statistical insignificance of the possible danger. Pauling, convinced that continued testing of weapons will only push us more rapidly down the road toward nuclear annihilation, counted every life sacrificed to the tests an inexcusable waste; he took the point of view that we should be cautious, should err on the side of pessimism, and laid stress on the number of victims rather than the small fraction of the population that they represent.

If such differences in points of view among scientists have caused public confusion, the Atomic Energy Commission, charged with responsibility for looking into these matters, has done little to dispel the confusion. Its public pronouncements seem to have been aimed at reassuring rather than informing.

However, the AEC attitude has been undergoing a change over the last few years. Evidence for this is found in statements by Willard Libby, who for several years was the Commission's chief spokesman in these matters. After the injection of the bomb-testing issue into the 1956 Presidential campaign, Dr. Libby wrote in *Science* (April 20, 1956):

On the basis of information so obtained, it is possible to say unequivocally that nuclear weapons tests carried out at the present time do not constitute a health hazard to the present population as far as radiostrontium is concerned.

Libby went on to say, in conclusion:

. . . the worldwide health hazards from the present rate of testing are insignificant.

But three years later, in a speech delivered at the University of Washington, Dr. Libby conceded:

It is, however, an area of uncertainty so large that only the most conservative treatment of the permissible body burdens of fallout isotopes is tolerable, and this conservative treatment indicates that care and caution must be taken about the matter of additional radioactive contamination.

During the three-year interval, the AEC had changed its public attitude toward the fallout problem. Perhaps it had been influenced by criticism of its position from the scientific community, but the main factor was the fact that bomb testing by the three nuclear powers since 1956 had more than doubled the global burden of fallout. The Commission no longer insisted on discussing the population exposure in terms of safeguards designed specifically for radiation workers but began to use the exposure limits recommended for large populations. After a year's delay, the AEC accepted the recommendation of the International Commission on Radiological Protection and lowered even the occupational limit by a factor of three.

Unfortunately the controversy over the consequences of testing has sometimes distorted the perspective in which it must be viewed. Fallout, after all, is but a by-product of our entry into the era of nuclear energy. From the processes in the submicroscopic world of the nucleus, man has begun to realize a source of energy which can forever release him from his anxious dependence on the dwindling fossil fuels and open an age in which the ocean itself will serve as his fuel reservoir. If wantonly released for destruction, however, the same energy could multiply the tragedy of Hiroshima and Nagasaki, where two small bombs,

500 times less powerful than a present-day hydrogen bomb, killed 100,000 people and injured 325,000.

There is the choice. Who must choose? In our democracy the course we take cannot be decided by scientists, nor should it be left to executive committees or military leaders. In our political system we rely on public opinion for guidance. Yet public opinion on the great nuclear questions remains largely unformed and uninformed. To present to the public the raw materials from which this opinion can be forged is both the privilege and the duty of the scientist. For in our world of complex knowledge and burgeoning technology, scientists have not one but two essential duties: first, the traditional duty of seeking the truth; secondly, the duty to communicate to all who need it the knowledge gained in their search.

The fallout problem highlights these two aspects of their function. Investigators in many fields of science have collected a vast amount of information about fallout. The information has been published in many technical papers and summarized in such useful reports as the two-volume compendium of hearings before the Joint Congressional Committee on Atomic Energy, under the title *The Nature of Radioactive Fallout and Its Effects on Man,* and in the report of the United Nations Scientific Committee on the Effects of Atomic Radiation. But these reports and summaries were written for experts; their technical vocabulary and style make them largely incomprehensible to the layman.

This book is an attempt to tell the facts in a more understandable form. The material to be covered is varied, spanning the fields of chemistry, physics, meteorology, biology, geology, and many others. Each chapter was written by an expert in a particular field. The first eight chapters describe nuclear weapons and the radioactive products of their explosions, the spread of this fallout over the earth, the paths it takes from soil to plant to man, the immediate and long-term effects of radiation upon man and upon his genetic constitution, and the possibility of protecting ourselves against these radiations. The remaining four chapters venture into more controversial subjects beyond the laboratory: the questions of civil defense, detection and inspection of bomb tests, and the overriding concern—the results of a nuclear war.

The object of the book is to inform, not to mold opinion. Its authors were selected for their knowledge of their subjects, not for their point of view; indeed, the editor does not know their specific stands on the question of suspending nuclear weapons tests. There has been no effort to arrive at a consensus of the contributors; each author is responsible only for the views expressed in his own chapter. What does firmly unite the contributors and the editor alike, however, is an awareness of the need for better public understanding of the scientific issues here discussed and a hope that their labors will contribute to such understanding.

1

JOHN M. FOWLER

The Bombs and
Their Products

Radioactivity is not new to man. The human species, like all forms of life on our planet, has evolved in an environment which has continually bombarded its cells with high-speed particles. This natural radioactivity comes from the air, the rocks and soil, the walls of buildings. Even our own bodies contain radioactive isotopes (*e.g.*, radioactive potassium) which have been present since the beginning of the universe. Besides these primordial sources, a steady rain of incredibly energetic cosmic rays, coming from somewhere deep in the vastness of our galaxy, is continually generating fresh radioactivity as it crashes into our atmosphere.

All this is known as the natural "background" of radiation to which life on our planet has been exposed for millions of years. But at the turn of our century man suddenly began to produce new radiations in the laboratory. Wilhelm Konrad Roentgen of Germany, experimenting with a beam of electrons, discovered that the impact of these particles on the walls of his tube created a mysterious radiation which he named X-rays. A few months later Henri Becquerel of France followed with his discovery of the radioactivity of uranium. Driven by an eager urge to explore these newest secrets of nature, scientists proceeded to experiment with more and more powerful sources of radiation.

At first they had no suspicion of danger. Roentgen delightedly made X-ray pictures of his wife's hand bones; experimenters enthusiastically gave themselves tremendous exposures, measuring the intensity of X-ray beams by sticking their hands in front of them; physicians and nurses worked with X-ray machines without any protection. Becquerel carried a vial of radium in his pocket for several days. Pierre Curie deliberately exposed a spot on his arm to radium for ten hours to study the biological effects—and reported that the rays produced a skin burn which took 52 days to heal.

Roentgen's discovery of the X-rays came late in the fall of 1895; by the following spring there were already published reports of burns and other injuries. Workers with the new radiations began to find that they caused warts and ulcers and even destroyed the fingers and hands. By 1902 the first cases of cancer from X-rays had been discovered; by the beginning of World War I there were more than 100 known cases and several deaths. Yet the problem was so little appreciated that as late as the 1920's and 1930's people were still drinking radium water as a cure for various diseases.

From the early days, however, a few alert investigators began to realize the great peril of such radiations and the need for protective measures. Elihu Thompson, an American designer of X-ray tubes, made himself a guinea pig by experimenting with exposures of his little finger, and from his experiments he derived some suggestions for protection. Gradually experimenters and physicians learned that elaborate precautions must be developed if man was to live safely with the intense radiations he had begun to create.

Scientists paid a heavy price for this knowledge; many lost their lives before the lessons were learned. The deaths of Marie Curie, her daughter Irène, Irène's husband Frédéric Joliot, and other pioneers in physics can be attributed in whole or in part to radiation overexposure. In Hamburg, Germany, there is a memorial inscribed: "To the Roentgenologists and Radiologists of all nations who have given their lives in the struggle against all diseases of mankind." The list contained 110 names when the memorial was erected in 1936, and it has grown longer since then.

The hazards of X-rays and radium, once understood, can be controlled. But with the discovery of fission and the explosion of the first atomic bomb, the hazard became general. Man-made radiation now began to pervade the atmosphere and man's whole environment. The contamination was extremely dilute, to be sure, but as the Alamogordo, Hiroshima, and Nagasaki bombs were followed after the war by scores of nuclear weapons tests by the United States, the U.S.S.R., and Great Britain, scientists grew more and more concerned about the steadily increasing rain of fallout.

Fission and Fusion Bombs

Let us begin our survey of the fallout phenomenon by considering the source—the bombs themselves. The fission and fusion bombs are no longer much of a secret: they have been rather thoroughly described—notably in publications outside the United States. Here, then, are the main features of the bombs. (The basic physical discoveries underlying their development are discussed in more detail in appendices at the end of the book.)

First, the fission bomb. Its paramount feature was, of course, its unprecedented energy. The so-called blockbusters of World War II—the biggest bombs of the old-fashioned chemical variety —contained about one ton of TNT. In contrast, the atomic bomb dropped on Hiroshima had the explosive force of 20,000 tons, yet the bomb itself, including its firing mechanism, probably weighed less than five tons. Thus its destructive power per ton of payload was about 4,000 times that of the TNT bomb. The key to this staggering release of energy lay in the unlocking of the previously untapped energy reservoir in the nucleus of the atom. The fission of one pound of uranium produces as much energy as the burning of 1,380 tons of coal, or the explosion of 9,000 tons of TNT.

This huge release of energy is accomplished through the capture of neutrons by the fuel—uranium 235 or plutonium 239. Upon absorbing a neutron, the U-235 nucleus splits in two and in the process releases two or three neutrons which can trigger further fissions of neighboring uranium nuclei. If the mass of uranium is big enough so that neutrons are captured by nuclei at a faster rate than they escape from the surface of the mass, a chain reaction develops, and the mass explodes.

If the critical mass were simply packed into a bomb casing, it would quickly be triggered to explode by a wandering neutron from the ever-present cosmic-ray debris. This would make a very unsatisfactory bomb. What is needed is an assembly of two or more separate sub-critical masses with a mechanism which can bring them together quickly on signal to form the critical mass.

At least two different devices have been used. One of these bombs is called "the thin man." It consists of a long pipe with chunks of fissionable material at its two ends. To set off the bomb, the two pieces are simply fired toward each other and form the critical mass when they meet in the middle of the barrel. This straightforward approach, however, is wasteful of the bomb material. More sophisticated and economical is the bomb called "the fat man." It employs "implosion" to bring the critical mass together. (The anatomy of "the fat man" was the "atomic secret" passed on to the Russians by the spy David Greenglass.) Figure 1 is a simplified sketch of how "the fat man" might be constructed. The fissionable material is in the form of a hollow ball. This sphere is surrounded by a shell of ordinary explosive, made up of accurately machined sections. When the triggering mechanism is set off, all the sections fire simultaneously and "implode" toward the center, collapsing the fissile ball. The fissile material is compressed into a dense, critical mass; while the pressure of the implosion holds the mass together, a heavy shower of neutrons from a small but intense neutron source at the center starts a fission chain reaction throughout the fissile fuel.

The bomb tested at Alamogordo and later used at Nagasaki was the "fat man," with plutonium as the fuel. The Hiroshima bomb was a "thin man" of uranium 235; its simple design was considered so certain to work that it was not tested beforehand.

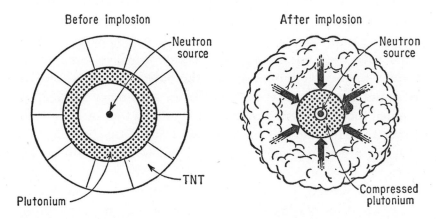

FIG. 1. The Fat Man.

The fusion bomb, better known as the hydrogen bomb, is a more elaborate affair. Its principle is simple enough. If the nuclei of two atoms of deuterium can be made to fuse, they will form a helium nucleus and release a great deal of energy (which is produced, as in fission, by conversion of a small part of the nuclear mass into energy). For example, the fusion of one pound of deuterium (the hydrogen isotope containing a proton and a neutron) yields an explosion equivalent to 11,000 tons of TNT. Furthermore, the product of this fusion, helium 3, can itself fuse with deuterium, so that the complete fusion of a pound of deuterium and its products would yield as much energy as 26,000 tons of TNT.

The complications of the fusion bomb arise from the fact that it takes a vast amount of energy to start the fusion reaction. To make deuterium nuclei fuse, for example, they must be heated to about 100 million degrees Fahrenheit. Such energy can be

provided by the explosion of a fission bomb, which can therefore serve as the trigger for a fusion bomb. But then comes the
problem of how to pack enough hydrogen fuel into the bomb
and how to hold it together long enough to allow it to fuse.

In the first attempt to solve this problem, the hydrogen was
condensed to its liquid form. This meant that it had to be reduced to a very low temperature—not far from absolute zero—
and so our first hydrogen "bomb" was a gigantic refrigerator,
weighing some 65 tons. Its fuel was tritium (the hydrogen isotope with one proton and two neutrons), which fuses more
readily than deuterium. This was the device detonated on the
island of Elugelab in the Marshalls on November 1, 1952. It
yielded the equivalent of about three million tons of TNT—150
times the Hiroshima bomb—and obliterated the little island,
gouging a gash one mile long and 175 feet deep in the ocean
bottom.

Having proved that a fission-fusion device would work, the
AEC scientists attacked the problem of reducing it to something
portable enough to be used as a bomb. Several scientists had
already suggested that the need for liquefying the hydrogen
might be avoided by combining it with the light metal lithium
in solid form; e.g., in the compound lithium deuteride, composed of one atom of lithium and one of deuterium. Lithium
itself could serve as part of the fuel material, for when the
isotope lithium 6 captures a neutron, its nucleus breaks down
into a nucleus of helium and one of hydrogen 3 (tritium). Triggered by the fireball of a fission bomb, a mass of lithium deuteride could give rise to a whole series of energy-generating reactions. The lithium 6 nucleus would split into nuclei of helium
and tritium, with an energy yield of 4.8 million electron volts
(Mev). Each tritium nucleus would fuse with deuterium to form
helium, yielding a neutron and 17.6 Mev of energy. Pairs of
deuterium nuclei would fuse in two ways, producing either
helium 3, with a yield of a neutron and 3.3 Mev of energy
($H^2 + H^2 \rightarrow He^3 + n$), or tritium and ordinary hydrogen
($H^2 + H^2 \rightarrow H^3 + H^1$), with a yield of 4 Mev. The series of

reactions would release a total of about 30 Mev of energy. Note also that two of the reactions produce neutrons. These are helpful as a neutron supply for the conversion of lithium to tritium. But they also yield a far more important dividend which led to a superbomb beyond all previous expectations. The way in which the neutrons were put to use to make the superbomb came to light as part of the tragic story of the *Lucky Dragon*.

The full story of this historic incident has been movingly told by Ralph Lapp in *The Voyage of the Lucky Dragon*. The unfortunate fishermen on the Japanese fishing vessel were showered with debris from our first superbomb, exploded at Bikini on the morning of March 1, 1954. At the time the outside world knew nothing about this bomb except that it was of the fusion type, and one aspect of its effects greatly puzzled physicists not connected with the project. A fusion bomb should be comparatively "clean"—that is, relatively low in fission products—yet the fallout from this bomb proved to be exceptionally "dirty"! The neutrons from the fusion reactions might be expected to produce some radioactivity in the bombarded coral, water, and air, but this effect would be much too small to account for the great load of radioactivity actually carried by the ashes of the Bikini explosion. What had made the bomb so dirty?

The answer was discovered by K. Kimura, one of the Japanese scientists who analyzed the fallout on the *Lucky Dragon's* deck. In this debris from the bomb he found a substantial amount of a rare isotope of uranium—uranium 237. It happened that Dr. Kimura himself was the original discoverer of this isotope; he had created it in the laboratory 14 years before and knew exactly how it was produced. It is a product of the bombardment of the common uranium isotope, 238, by neutrons. When uranium 238 captures a neutron of considerable energy, it becomes unstable, emits two neutrons and thus decays to uranium 237. But there is also another possibility: capture of a very high-energy neutron (more than one Mev), can cause the U-238 nucleus to fission like U-235.

So the finding of uranium 237 in the debris from the Bikini bomb solved the mystery of its dirty fallout and gave an unmistakable clue to its construction. The bomb must have had a thick blanket of uranium 238 surrounding its fission-fusion core; fast neutrons from the fusion reactions fissioned the U-238 blanket and thus multiplied the force of the bomb—and also the output of fission products. In short, the weapon builders had found a way to use the neutrons that would otherwise have gone to waste: they had made a fission-fusion-fission bomb in which common uranium 238 was added to the fuel. The March 1, 1954, bomb probably consisted of a 220-pound core of uranium 235, about the same weight of lithium deuteride and several thousand pounds of uranium 238. The total energy of the bomb was equivalent to 15 to 20 million tons (megatons) of TNT; of this about two megatons came from fusion, the rest from fission.

One can immediately see a great gain in economy over the "primitive" Hiroshima bomb. To produce a 20-megaton explosion with only the original fuel, uranium 235, would require 11,000 pounds (assuming an explosion efficiency of 20 per cent) of this rare isotope, separated so laboriously from U-238, and would cost about a hundred million dollars. Using U-238 as fuel, however, we can get our 20 megatons at the bargain-basement price of a quarter of a million dollars. (The same size of explosion with TNT would cost ten billion dollars!) Thus the attractiveness of the fission-fusion-fission bomb to military leaders is obvious, especially if we add to the economic advantage the further advantage that construction and delivery of the bomb are simplified because one can pack in any amount of U-238 without worrying about critical mass.

Blast and Heat

Let us now look at the several effects of a nuclear bomb. Its explosion differs from that of the ordinary TNT bomb both in character and in quantity—by many orders of magnitude. For instance, the temperature of the gases in a TNT explosion is at most about 9,000 degrees F., whereas the fireball of a nuclear bomb exceeds 100,000,000 degrees. The best way to get some notion of the incredible results is to follow the development of one of these explosions. The AEC has given detailed descriptions of nuclear bomb bursts in its report, *The Effects of Nuclear Weapons*. We shall take for illustration the explosion of a one-megaton bomb in the air.

The explosion takes place in less than a microsecond (millionth of a second). In that time the material of the bomb—fuel, mechanisms, casing, etc.—is completely vaporized to a hot gas with a pressure of several billion atmospheres. Within a few thousandths of a second it forms the roughly spherical, brightly growing fireball now so well known from pictures of atomic bombs. Although the fireball rapidly radiates heat away from its surface, even after about a hundredth of a second it is still 30 times brighter than the midday sun (to an observer as far as 60 miles away).

At this point the fireball of a one-megaton bomb is about 440 feet in diameter; it will grow to 7,200 feet (nearly a mile and a half across) after ten seconds. As it expands, it also rises like a hot-air balloon, starting at 300 miles per hour and gradually slowing down. After six minutes it has soared to 14 miles above the earth. But long before it reaches this height it has lost its incandescence and become a cloud of condensed particles. The cloud at first is reddish in color, because it contains a considerable amount of compounds of nitrogen—mainly nitric acid, formed from nitrogen and oxygen (it is estimated that a one-megaton explosion creates about 5,000 tons of this extremely corrosive acid).

As water vapor condenses, the cloud gradually becomes white. On reaching the stratosphere, the head of the cloud spreads out in the familiar mushroom shape; it also thrusts into the stratosphere as high as 25 miles above the earth.

Let us now consider in a bit more detail the forms of energy released in the bomb. In a typical air burst, 50 per cent of the energy goes into blast, or pressure waves, 35 per cent into heat radiation, and the remaining 15 per cent into radioactivity.

The shock front of the blast wave breaks away from the fireball about one tenth of a second after the explosion and spreads like a ripple at a little above the speed of sound. The wave from a one-megaton burst is about 1,000 feet deep, and so can engulf most buildings. It squeezes them as a gigantic fist would. With the shock front go winds as strong as 180 miles per hour in the first few seconds. The blast from a bomb of this energy almost completely destroys all buildings within two miles of the explosion, and severely damages everything but massive buildings up to three miles. The range of destruction is proportional to the cube root of the bomb's energy; thus the devastation by blast from a 20-megaton bomb would reach ten times farther than that of the 20,000-ton Hiroshima bomb.

The bomb's heat radiation is no less staggering. A one-megaton bomb produces a flash hot enough to convert more than a billion pounds of water into steam. It can cause third-degree burns to a person 13 miles away; a 20-megaton bomb would extend third-degree burns to 45 miles.

The Radioactive Products

But our main concern here is the radioactivity. As we have seen, this lies principally in the fission products from the splitting of uranium or plutonium. The millions upon millions of nuclei fissioned give birth to a multitude of particles of many varieties of radioactivity; in all, some 200 different radioactive isotopes emerge from a fission explosion. Some are intensely active but short-lived; some will go on spewing radiation for hundreds or thousands of years.

We must briefly examine the nature of these radiations. First, there are the high-speed beta particles, or electrons, which are emitted by most fission products. These particles cannot penetrate far into matter and therefore produce little damage—at worst, skin ulcers—when they attack the body from outside. But if a beta-emitter gets inside the body, it can cause serious injury to the sensitive tissues there. Strontium 90, the most feared of the fission products, is a beta-emitter and enters the body via milk and other foods. Secondly, there are the alpha particles, another product of the decay of radioactive isotopes, including radium. Carrying twice the charge of electrons and 4,000 times more massive, they are stopped by matter even more quickly, but like the beta particles they become a serious menace inside the body. Thirdly, a nuclear explosion and its debris release gamma rays. This radiation is similar to X-rays but is more energetic. Its high penetrating power makes it dangerous from outside the body as well as within. Among the fallout products are many gamma-emitters, and of these cesium 137 is particularly feared as a long-term hazard.

The intensity of radiation from a nuclear explosion is so vast as to numb the mind. From a one-megaton bomb, the gamma radiation an hour after the explosion is equivalent to the radioactivity of 300,000 tons of radium! And the various kinds of radiation continue to be released in large amounts for a very long time. Strontium 90 is produced in such quantities that 30 years after the explosion the undecayed strontium 90 still left in the world will amount to as much activity as that of 200 pounds of radium.

The radioactive debris from a bomb burst is swept skyward and sets forth on various journeys which will depend on the size of the particles, the vagaries of the weather, and so on. Some of the deadly dust will fall to the ground in the vicinity of the explosion within ten hours. Some will ride the winds for several weeks. And some will rise to the stratosphere and fall out months or years later on the other side of the world. Chapter 2 discusses the meteorological factors that shape the pattern of fallout.

The amount and distribution of radioactivity depend of course on whether the bomb is exploded in the air, on the ground, or under water. We also have some information on what happens when nuclear bombs are detonated in outer space above the earth's atmosphere, thanks to the famous high-altitude "Argus" tests of 1958. In such an explosion we must expect about half of the high-speed fission particles to be propelled away from the earth and the other half toward the earth, so that the latter will eventually fall to the ground. The most interesting fact discovered in the Argus project was that beta particles from the fission products are trapped in the earth's magnetic field and form a band of electrons 300 or 400 miles above the earth's surface.

The "Clean" Bomb

We have examined the radioactive output of fission bombs; now let us look at the question of the so-called "clean" bomb. A clean bomb would be one depending almost entirely on fusion. The AEC has reported bomb tests which were 96 per cent "clean" (apparently in comparison with the dirty March 1, 1954, bomb). But a completely clean bomb is an obvious impossibility. To begin with, a fusion bomb requires a fission bomb as its trigger. And we must also remember those neutrons that the fusion bomb releases in copious quantities. Neutrons, bombarding the surroundings, transform atoms of the air, earth, water and the bomb material itself into radioactive isotopes. In amount, this induced radioactivity is insignificant compared to the fission products. But it may have some peculiarly dangerous consequences.

The ash that fell on the *Lucky Dragon* contained radioactive calcium produced by neutrons in the coral island blown up by the bomb. Another product of the neutrons was discovered when clams in the waters of the Marshall Islands were found to be highly radioactive. The shellfish were contaminated with radioactive cobalt 60; they had concentrated it from the sea water, where neutrons had converted the scarce atoms of normal cobalt 59 into the radioactive isotope. This discovery illustrates an important fact about fallout: although it is highly diluted in the air, soil, or water, it may be collected in danger-ous concentrations by plants or animals taking up certain ele-ments as food.

The most important of the neutron-produced substances is radioactive carbon 14. Carbon is a prime constituent of living matter, and it makes up 18 per cent of the human body. It therefore became a matter of concern when the monitors of fallout discovered that the fusion bombs were creating carbon 14 in significant amounts.

Physicists—and also archaeologists—were already well ac-quainted with carbon 14. It is constantly being created in the atmosphere by the cosmic-ray bombardment: neutrons knocked out of atoms by this bombardment are captured by nitrogen in the air, and the nitrogen is converted to carbon 14. The carbon in the atmosphere, in the form of carbon dioxide, finds its way into all living organisms. They go on taking in fresh carbon as long as they live, but after death ends this uptake, the amount of radiocarbon in their remains diminishes steadily by radio-active decay. The half-life of carbon 14 is 5,600 years (*i.e.*, in 5,600 years half of the nuclei have shed their beta particles and become something else—in this case, nitrogen again). It was from these facts and this train of thought that Willard Libby at the University of Chicago drew his brilliant inspiration for using radiocarbon as a clock for dating ancient remains.

Our bodies, then, have always contained some cosmic-ray carbon 14. Now this radioactive load has been increased by the bomb-generated radiocarbon. We can make an estimate of the amount of carbon 14 created on the basis of estimates of the number of neutrons released in the bomb explosions. Argonne scientists have looked for the answer in a more direct way by measuring the carbon 14 in air samples taken by balloons. They find that the carbon 14 in the lower atmosphere has been in-creasing at the rate of about 3 per cent per year since 1954 (see Figure 2). In the stratosphere, which still holds most of the radiocarbon produced, the carbon 14 content in 1959 was four and one half times the normal level. All in all, it is estimated that the bomb tests added 1,300 pounds of radiocarbon to the 1,900 pounds normally in the atmosphere. (It is ironic that Libby, as a member of the AEC, was partly responsible for the bomb tests which added so much artificial carbon 14 to the atmosphere and thus fouled up the future use of his dating method.)

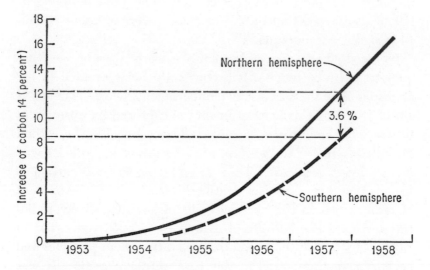

FIG. 2. Increase of radioactive carbon in the earth's atmosphere since hydrogen-bomb testing began. The 1953 starting point represents the normal level of natural carbon 14 from cosmic rays.

On the whole we must conclude that there can be no really clean bomb, even in theory. The fact is that up to the suspension of tests in the fall of 1958 the radioactive pollution of our atmosphere by the nuclear powers continued at an accelerating pace. In hearings before the Special Subcommittee on Radiation of the Joint Congressional Committee on Atomic Energy in the spring of 1959, an AEC spokesman gave figures on the total yields of the 203 nuclear weapons exploded up to that time by the United States, Great Britain, and the U.S.S.R. They are summarized in the following table.

	FISSION YIELD (kilotons)		FUSION YIELD	TOTAL	FISSION, PER CENT OF TOTAL
	U.S. and Great Britain	U.S.S.R.	U.S.,Great Britain, and U.S.S.R.		
1945–1951	700	60	0	760	100
1952–1954	37,000	500	22,500	60,000	63
1955–1956	9,200	4,000	14,800	28,000	47
1957–1958	19,000	21,000	45,000	85,000	47
Totals	65,900	25,560	82,300	173,760	

In short, of the 174 million tons of nuclear energy released in the bomb tests up to the end of 1958, about 92 million tons came from fission explosions. Analyzing the progress of the tests, one is struck by two things. In the first place, in the year of the testing of the "clean" bomb by the United States (1957–1958) fission still accounted for half the total yield of the nuclear powers' bomb tests: the typical bomb was still a dirty one. In the second place, the figures show that the 1957–1958 tests put out almost as much fission debris as all the tests that had gone before; in other words, these latest tests nearly doubled the radioactive pollution of our atmosphere.

2

LESTER MACHTA
ROBERT J. LIST

The Global Pattern
of Fallout

What happens to the radioactive debris of a nuclear bomb after it is injected into the atmosphere? Does it spread more or less uniformly over the globe, or does it tend to concentrate in certain zones? Obviously we need an answer to this question if we are to attempt to predict how much radiation the world's population centers will receive. Can meteorology supply the answer?

We can divide fallout into three categories: local, tropospheric, and stratospheric. The local fallout consists of the heaviest particles in the bomb debris, which fall out within the first day or so in the vicinity of the explosion. From a small bomb, the local fallout may cover only a few miles; in the case of a big explosion (in the megaton range) on a windy day, it may reach several hundred miles downwind. The local fallout will be particularly heavy if the bomb is exploded at low altitude, so that the fireball sucks up material from the ground.

Of the remaining bomb cloud—consisting of particles so light that they will fall to the ground only when washed down by rain or snow—part will stay in the troposphere and part will rise to the stratosphere. The troposphere is the layer of the atmosphere extending up 35,000 to 55,000 feet, depending on season and latitude; it contains our everyday weather. On its prevailing west-east winds, the tropospheric fallout is carried rapidly around the world and is soon washed down; about half the debris in the troposphere falls out each month. It does not have time to drift far in the north-south direction, and so the tropospheric radioactivity falls out at about the same latitude as the bomb explosion.

There is good reason to believe that a major part of the debris from the more powerful bombs is thrust into the stratosphere. In that cloudless, nonturbulent region of the atmosphere the circulation is undoubtedly different from the east-west currents of the troposphere. What sort of pattern of air movement can we expect there?

Over the past ten years two British scientists, A. W. Brewer and G. M. B. Dobson, have developed a plausible picture of the stratospheric circulation. They considered the question: Why is the air in the stratosphere so much drier than in the troposphere? A boundary called the tropopause separates the stratosphere from the troposphere. In the earth's equatorial belt, the tropopause is extremely cold (about 112 degrees below zero F.) —colder than any other part of our atmosphere. Brewer and Dobson concluded that the equatorial tropopause must be the main gateway through which air enters the stratosphere from the troposphere, for this very cold filter would dry the air most effectively. If air comes into the stratosphere near the Equator, it probably moves toward the poles and sinks back into the troposphere in the temperate or polar latitudes, thus establishing a north-south circulation.

Brewer and Dobson reasoned further that the sinking of the stratospheric air must be most pronounced in the late winter or early spring, when the air in the high latitudes is coldest, and therefore heaviest. They saw support for this theory in the fact that there is a seasonal cycle in the amounts of ozone in the troposphere of the temperate and polar latitudes. Ozone is produced mainly in the stratosphere.

All this suggests a general model of the circulation. Imagine a fountain of moist tropical air rising slowly toward the stratosphere in the low latitudes near the Equator. When it reaches the tropopause, it is wrung dry of its moisture by condensation in that cold boundary layer. After passing into the stratosphere, the air mass moves slowly toward the pole of its hemisphere (northward in the Northern Hemisphere, southward in the Southern). Months or years later it descends into the troposphere again somewhere in the temperate or polar regions; this sinking is accelerated in late winter or spring.

The Travels of Fallout

What fallout predictions does this circulation suggest? In the first place, since each hemisphere has a separate circulation, we should expect most of the debris from a bomb to fall out in the same hemisphere in which it is exploded (see Figure 3). Consequently the fallout from the bomb tests, nearly all of which took place in the Northern Hemisphere, should be deposited mainly in that hemisphere, though some of it may cross the Equator through mixing of the stratospheric air between the two hemispheres. The model predicts further that the fallout will be heaviest in the temperate latitudes (which have more precipitation than the polar regions). The greatest amount of fallout should come in late winter or spring. Finally, the model suggests that bombs exploded in the temperate or polar latitudes will deposit their fallout sooner than those near the Equator. Bomb debris thrust into the stratosphere near the Equator travels a long journey before it re-enters the troposphere in the poleward latitudes; in contrast, an explosion near the Arctic is in the region of sinking air, and the debris therefore should return to the troposphere more quickly. To translate this into concrete terms: the Russian fallout should come down much faster than the American, because the Soviet testing grounds are north of the 60-degree latitude while the main American tests took place at the latitude of 11 degrees in the Pacific.

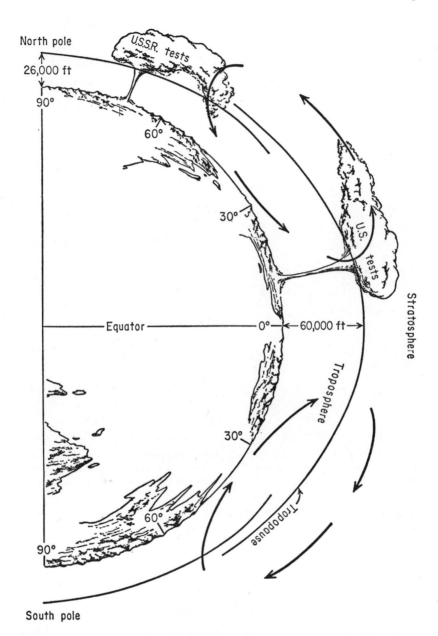

FIG. 3. Model of the air circulation between the troposphere and the stratosphere, showing the probable routes of global travel of fallout. Most of the large United States bomb tests took place at tropical latitudes; the Soviet tests, at northerly latitudes.

Let us now see how well the Brewer-Dobson model agrees with measurements of fallout samples taken around the world. Strontium 90 serves as a good marker for the fallout. The best world-wide collection of samples of strontium 90 levels in the soil has been assembled by Lyle T. Alexander of the United States Department of Agriculture. We have plotted the soil samples for the spring of 1958 on a graph (see Figure 4). Mak-

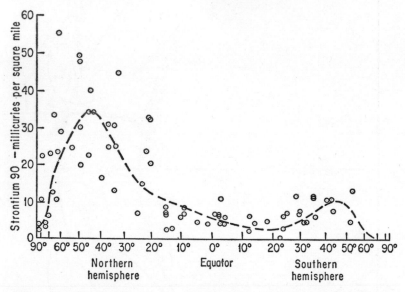

FIG. 4. Strontium 90 fallout in the soil, according to world-wide measurements in the spring of 1958. Each dot represents a soil sample at the given latitude. The variations within each belt are accounted for by rainfall differences and other local conditions.

ing allowances for local variations in rainfall, we can draw a curve depicting the average fallout according to latitude. It shows clearly that the peak of strontium 90 fallout comes in the temperate latitudes of the Northern Hemisphere, as the Brewer-Dobson model predicts. However, this is the total fallout—combining the tropospheric and the stratospheric. To test the Brewer-Dobson theory of the stratospheric circulation we must subtract the tropospheric fallout. The amount of this fallout—i.e., bomb debris which never reaches the stratosphere and comes down within a few weeks—can be estimated from the sizes and altitudes of the bomb explosions, the proportion of short-lived isotopes in the fallout, and other indications. It turns out that only a small part of the global fallout is tropospheric; most of it seems to be definitely stratospheric. When we subtract the tropospheric part, we find that the profile of the stratospheric fallout still shows a pronounced peak in the North temperate latitudes. There is also a small peak in the temperate latitudes of the Southern Hemisphere, which demonstrates that some bomb debris does travel across the Equator via the stratosphere.

Thus the pattern of fallout in the soil agrees well with the Brewer-Dobson model. We can apply a second test. Instead of the accumulation in the soil, let us take the *rate* of fallout, as measured in rainfall. This information should give us not only independent evidence on the geographical pattern but also a test of the prediction that fallout will be heaviest in the late winter or spring.

We have analyzed measurements of the strontium 90 fallout in rain which were collected by the United States and Great Britain at a number of stations around the world during the period from July, 1957, through June, 1958—a period of many bomb tests. Again, subtracting the tropospheric fallout, we find that the stratospheric fallout shows the same profile as in the soil samples; that is, a strong peak in the Northern Hemisphere mid-latitudes.

For seasonal variations, we can consult the records of New York City, which has kept the longest watch on fallout of any station in the United States. The New York Office of the Atomic Energy Commission has been measuring the strontium 90 in rain each month since the beginning of 1954. Its month-by-month "rainout" record is shown in Figure 5. Most striking is the fact that there are annual peaks of fallout which do indeed tend to come in late winter or spring. This higher fallout in the spring is not necessarily associated with heavier rainfall: it occurs even when rainfall is below normal. And most of it is clearly stratospheric. Indeed, there is evidence that the short-term fallout

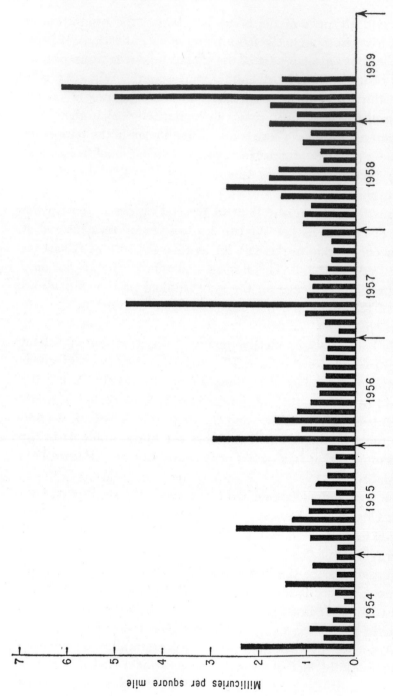

FIG. 5. Strontium 90 in rainfall at New York City, as measured month by month since 1954. There is a marked seasonal effect, the fallout being heaviest in early spring.

from the troposphere plays little part in the seasonal cycle. In 1957, when the United States ran a series of bomb tests in Nevada from June to September, the fallout rate in New York nevertheless showed its usual summer and autumn decline. This tends to confirm that the stratospheric storage and circulation probably play the major role in the seasonal variability of fallout.

Stations in other countries, at about the same latitude as New York, also show a spring peak. But all this evidence is still not conclusive proof that the Brewer-Dobson model is correct. One may argue that perhaps the spring rains in the North temperate latitudes are somehow more efficient than rain at other times and places in scavenging the bomb debris from the atmosphere. So we subjected the model to a third test; namely, the distribution of radioactive debris in the air itself. Fortunately there are records of this also: the United States Naval Research Laboratory has collected measurements of fission-product concentrations in the air at many places around the world.

In Figure 6 we have plotted sample measurements for four successive months in the winter and spring of 1958—January, February, March, and April. Once again we see the same sort of profile, featured by high peaks of radioactivity in the North temperate zone. These peaks, falling in the latitudes between 20 and 40 degrees, are slightly south of those in the soil and rainfall profiles, but this may be explainable by the fact that along the United States East Coast, where the air measurements were made, the belt of maximum storminess is displaced southward from the world average.

Even this single-season record shows the seasonal trend predicted by the Brewer-Dobson model. In the Northern Hemisphere, the amount of strontium 90 in the tropospheric air increased from winter (January) to spring (April); contrariwise, in the Southern Hemisphere it declined from summer (January) to autumn (April).

The most convincing evidence of all in favor of the Brewer-Dobson picture came as a result of a tracer experiment generated by the bomb tests in the Marshall Islands in the summer of 1958. These explosions created a new radioactive product, tungsten 185, which had not been found in any previous test. During the following January, measurable amounts of this substance were turning up in the air in both the Northern and Southern Hemispheres. Presumably, considering the lapse of time, most of it had journeyed through the stratosphere. By January there was very little tungsten 185 in the equatorial latitudes where the explosions had taken place, but peak con-

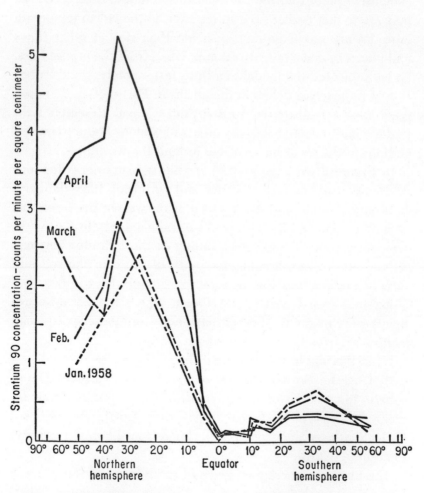

FIG. 6. Strontium 90 in the air, as measured in air samples collected by the United States Naval Research Laboratory in four successive months in 1958.

centrations of it appeared in the North temperate zone, the same region in which strontium 90 also is at a maximum. There was also a small peak in the temperate latitudes of the Southern Hemisphere.

In short, the tungsten 185, serving as a tracer in the air, showed the route of bomb-debris travel in the clearest possible fashion. Most of this debris stayed in the Northern Hemisphere and must have traveled northward via the stratosphere.

Measurements of radioactivity in the air also seem to tell us something else. In October, 1958, the Soviet Union detonated a series of massive fission explosions at its far northern testing grounds. These probably increased the amount of fission products in the stratosphere by two and a half times. By the following March the fission-product radioactivity of the lower air in the North temperate regions had jumped disproportionately. That is to say, the Russian fallout seemed to be coming out faster than that from previous (American) explosions. Furthermore, there was no significant increase in the Southern Hemisphere. Several uncertainties make the interpretation of these facts inconclusive, but tentatively they appear to support the picture of the circulation and the consequent prediction about the speed of Russian fallout which we discussed early in this chapter.

The Brewer-Dobson picture is not accepted by all meteorologists. It still presents some unresolved questions, and other theories might account for the observed fallout pattern. But at the moment we think this model of the circulation provides the best explanation of the facts as we know them.

Consequences

Assuming that the model is correct, we can draw certain conclusions about the practical consequences. First, the radioactive bomb debris still in the atmosphere will fall out most heavily in the temperate latitudes of the Northern Hemisphere, where most of the world's population is concentrated. The fallout hazard in this belt is and will continue to be at least two and a half times as great as the global average, and local variations will make the hazard still greater for some populations. Secondly, the exceptionally rapid fallout from the massive Russian tests of 1958 will increase the discrepancy, raising the exposure of the Northern mid-latitudes to more than two and a half times the world average. This fast fallout may also heighten the danger from short-lived fission products, which would spend their radiation harmlessly if they remained in the stratosphere for a year or more.

3

W. O. CASTER

From Bomb
to Man

The years since Hiroshima have served to deepen the apprehension with which mankind first received the news of the birth of the Atomic Age on August 6, 1945. Although people have tried to put from their minds the picture of the city-flattening blast and the searing fireball that demolished Hiroshima, the radiation effects have lingered on as an ever-present reminder. A decade after the bombing, scores of Hiroshima citizens were dying each year of leukemia and other diseases attributed by Japanese doctors to the bomb's radiation. On August 6, 1957, the twelfth anniversary of the bombing, 20,000 citizens assembled in the rebuilt city's Peace Memorial Park heard their Mayor, Tabao Wantanabe, declare:

> It is only a foolish illusion to try to maintain peace by the might of possessing atom and hydrogen bombs, and experimenting with them. Present tests of nuclear weapons are undermining the existence of mankind. Radioactive elements, once taken inside the body, not only corrode from within but continue wreaking genetic havoc with the offspring.

Hiroshima and Nagasaki are not the only places in the world where people have experienced fallout and are acutely sensitive to this hazard. There have been a series of incidents, some of which evoked profound panic: the *Lucky Dragon* incident, the Windscale reactor accident in England, the fallout scares in Nevada and California. In the summer of 1957 a rainfall in the corn and wheat belts of the midwestern United States carried enough fallout to rattle Geiger counters at rates as high as a million counts per minute per gallon of rain. In that case there was no panic: the public was not told until months later. But the effect was to create a feeling of distrust.

From these incidents and from experimental work on laboratory animals we have learned some of the basic chemical and biological facts about fallout: what it is, how it gets to man, and what it does after it gets there. In this chapter we shall try to trace out the devious and complex route by which fallout enters our bodies, and where it concentrates after entering them.

Early Fallout

There are two types of fallout, early and late, and they have quite different biological effects. The debris from an atomic bomb explosion is a mixture of radioactive material of many kinds: particles of unfissioned uranium or plutonium, fission products, and many other radioisotopes created by the neutrons. Of the nearly 200 isotopes emerging, 70 per cent are short-lived materials with half-lives of less than one day. The radiation from the bomb cloud in the first few hours is indescribably intense: a cloud of fission particles one hour old can be likened to a mammoth X-ray machine pouring out a lethal beam of gamma radiation. And large particles falling out of the cloud in the early stage are emitting beta radiation intense enough to burn the skin.

If we were to follow that cloud of fresh fission products, we would find that the intensity of radiation decreased by one third in the first seven hours and by another third in seven days. The remaining third of the radiation would be released in progressively decreasing amounts over a long period, some small amount remaining even after millions of years.

Within the first few hours after bomb detonation the major hazard of fallout is exposure of the whole body to gamma radiation. The effects are in every way analogous to those seen after exposure of the total body to X-rays. In case of a nuclear attack this early fallout near the sites of bomb detonation would pose the greatest hazard. It is this brief period of intense and penetrating environmental radiation that determines how soon one can move troops through a bombed area or order a crew into an airport to start decontamination procedures. The completeness with which these considerations dominate military thinking can be seen in a statement which General Curtis LeMay made to the Senate Committee on Air Power:

> Now fallout is not the horrible thing that some people might lead us to believe, in that if you can just get under a couple or three feet of ground, just in a basement or something like that, and stay there for a while until this hot air has cooled off a little bit—and the air cools off rapidly—then you can get out.

This is also the rationale of the Civil Defense proposals concerning the construction of bomb shelters and the instructions that people should seek refuge in a basement. It is true that a few feet of earth or concrete can furnish almost complete protection against lethal intensities of gamma radiation. By remaining in such a shelter for the few hours or days required for the fresh fission products to dissipate the major part of their activity, one could escape this hazard.

Long-Term Fallout

But there is another aspect to the fallout problem, and this relates to the part of the fallout energy that is still being released weeks, months, or years after the bomb explosion. We refer to late fallout effects. The residue of long-lived isotopes is very small in amount. Its biological effect is completely trivial *so long as it stays outside the body*. But if the radioactive particles enter the body, in the food and drinking water we ingest, in the air we breathe, or through the skin, it becomes a hazard. Once one emerges from the bomb shelter, he has the immediate and long-range problem of obtaining food and drinking water. Everything that he touches is radioactive.

The long-lived isotopes that are the chief cause for concern are strontium 90 (together with the radioactive daughter to which it decays, yttrium 90), cesium 137 (and its radioactive daughter barium 137), cerium 144 (and its daughter praseodymium 144), carbon 14, and unfissioned uranium and plutonium. There are also some particularly damaging isotopes, such as iodine, cobalt, and strontium 89, which are fairly short-lived but are produced in such large quantities in the bomb tests that they must be considered. These hazardous isotopes, and the parts of the body in which they are concentrated and against which they direct their attack, are listed in the table below. Note that elements such as strontium, uranium, and plutonium are especially dangerous because they are bone-seekers and can become fixed in the bones of the body and remain there for many years.

PART OF BODY ATTACKED	ISOTOPE
Skeleton	Calcium—45
	Strontium—89 and 90
	Yttrium—90 and 91
	Barium—140
	Lanthanum—140
	Uranium and Plutonium
Thyroid	Iodine—131, 132, 133, and 135
Liver	Manganese—56
	Cobalt—60
	Cerium—141 and 144
	Praseodymium—143 and 144
	Neodymium—147
Whole Body	Cesium—137
	Carbon—14

Once a radioactive isotope has been taken into the body, the amount of damage it will do depends on its physical half-life (*i.e.*, rate of radioactive decay) and also on its "biological half-life," meaning the average length of stay of the substance in the body. In the case of substances which have a comparatively rapid rate of exchange in the body's metabolism, the radioisotope is soon excreted. For example, the biological half-life of carbon in the human body is about six months; on the average, an atom of radioactive carbon 14 incorporated in body tissue will be eliminated after about six months. On the other hand, an atom of strontium 90 built into bone, where the rate of mineral exchange is very slow, may not be eliminated during a person's lifetime. The physical and biological half-lives of some of the more important radioisotopes are given in the table below. The two types of half-life are related, because when a radioactive atom undergoes physical decay, its biological life of course also ceases.

HALF-LIFE IN YEARS

	Physical	*Biological*
Strontium 90	28	10
Strontium 89	0.1	0.1
Cesium 137	30	0.05
Carbon 14	5,600	0.5
Plutonium	24,000	100
Uranium 235	100,000	0.5

It is the ability of some radioisotopes to masquerade as their close chemical cousins (*e.g.*, strontium 90 as calcium, radioactive iodine as natural iodine, cesium 137 as potassium), and thus be absorbed into the body, that makes them particularly dangerous. The body has very efficient mechanisms for capturing iodine and concentrating it in the thyroid gland, for directing calcium and other bone-seeking elements to the skeleton and holding them there, and for concentrating other elements at specific points. Consequently the full destructive force of a radioactive material may focus on a single organ.

Large amounts of radioactivity concentrated in the skeleton

can damage the bone marrow to produce anemias and leukemias, and can damage the bone-forming cells to produce bone
cancer. This latter is a slow process and requires high doses of
radiation. In the case of bone cancer, the patient may not be
aware of any abnormality or discomfort for 15 to 20 years after
the exposure. When symptoms do appear and the diagnosis is
made, the life expectancy may be only a few years. In short,
radiation damage frequently requires many years to become
evident. This fact helps to explain why scientists cannot say
with certainty what levels of radiation are hazardous—and in
truth will not know for many years.

Uptake of Strontium 90

Strontium 90 is considered to be the most hazardous of the
bone-seeking fission products, because of its long half-life and
because it resembles calcium so closely. When strontium 90
falls to earth, it becomes mixed with calcium and follows calcium through its ecological chain in nature. The strontium 90
that settles on vegetation may remain as a surface contaminant
or may be absorbed through the leaves. The strontium 90 that
reaches the soil becomes mixed with the available calcium in
that soil and can be taken up with calcium through the root
system and fed to all parts of the plant. From plants that form
a part of the human diet we then obtain strontium 90 directly.
This pathway also brings strontium 90 into the diet of grazing
animals. It then becomes incorporated into the bone, meat, and
milk of these animals and thus into the human diet.

Careful studies of the movements of strontium 90 in the
calcium cycle of nature reveal that, at many points in this cycle,
organisms are able to distinguish between strontium and calcium. In most cases, fortunately, the tendency is to concentrate
the calcium and reject the strontium. This process of differential
absorption has been termed "discrimination." A measure
of the amount of discrimination occurring in any case is

obtained by observing the decrease in the amount of strontium 90 associated with each gram of calcium. In effect, one
considers that strontium 90 is a contaminant of natural calcium.
Then, as one follows calcium from soil to plant to farm animal
and finally to man, the progressive decrease in the amount of
strontium 90 associated with each gram of calcium is a measure
of the discrimination at each selective biological stage. The
strontium 90 concentration per gram of calcium in the human
skeleton is perhaps tenfold lower than that in the plants and
soil in any given area.

Recent studies make it possible to point to a number of the
specific places in the ecological chain at which discrimination
occurs and to give some general rules relating to the amount of
discrimination that can be expected in a given instance. The
first step at which scientists thought they might find discrimination against strontium was in the processes of uptake by
plants. But studies of this step in the chain have revealed more
puzzles than answers. In some experiments it appears that the
plant may tend to reject strontium. More frequently, however,
the ratio of strontium to calcium is much greater in the plant
than in the soil in which it grew. Apparently there are two
explanations of this: the plant may absorb fallout directly into
its leaves as well as from the soil, and plants with shallow roots
may absorb freshly fallen strontium before it has become generally mixed in the soil. In general, the concentration of strontium
in plants is found to vary with the species of plant, the type of
soil, the drainage conditions, and the geographical region.
Within a plant, there is also wide variation in the uptake of
strontium by different parts: the leafy portions (which make
up the major source of plant food for grazing farm animals)
seem to have higher concentrations than the grain and fruit
portions.

Could the uptake of strontium by plants be reduced by di-
luting the strontium in the soil with heavy applications of
calcium? Experiments have been tried along this line. But even
drastic liming of the soil, to the point of decreasing its fertility,

has not been very effective: it cuts the strontium concentration in plants by only about one half.

The major discrimination, or strontium "filtering," comes in the animals that eat the plants. Their digestive and metabolic processes tend to select calcium and reject strontium, with the result that the original strontium-calcium ratio in their feed is reduced to about one fourth in their meat and eggs and to perhaps one tenth in their milk. This has important implications for the human diet. Milk, for instance, has a smaller concentration of strontium 90 than vegetables do. Thus milk is our safest and best source of calcium.

In the typical American diet, dairy products furnish about 80 per cent of the calcium. On the other hand, in parts of the world where milk is not readily available, most of the calcium in the diet comes from plant sources. In Japan, for example, where the major components of the diet are rice and fish, about 70 per cent of the dietary calcium is furnished by plant foods. The result is a two- to threefold increase in the amount of strontium 90 contamination associated with each gram of dietary calcium.

After eating radioactively contaminated food, the human body itself tends to reject strontium through its own filtering system. We find that the concentration of strontium 90 deposited with calcium in the bones is only one fourth to one half that in the diet. Part of the selective process seems to take place in the digestive tract, part in the kidney, part in the skeleton. In a child, who is rapidly laying down bone mineral, the amount of strontium 90 per gram of calcium in newly formed bone is about one half that in his food. The sites of discrimination here are probably the kidney and digestive tract. In the adult the discrimination appears to be somewhat greater: he filters out three fourths of the strontium 90 concentration in his diet. This additional discrimination presumably arises from the fact that the slow recrystallization of bone mineral in the adult is a more selective process and incorporates less strontium 90 than does the rapidly growing bone of a child.

The Radiation Dose

In spite of the filtering processes, strontium 90 remains one of the most hazardous of the fallout products. How can the hazard be measured? When a radiobiologist is asked to evaluate the hazard from a radioactive substance, he asks four questions: (1) What type of radiation does it emit, and what is its energy? (2) What is its physical half-life? (3) Is the material readily absorbed by the body, and if so, how long does it stay? (4) Is it concentrated at any point within the body, and if so, where and to what extent?

First of all, strontium 90 is an energetic emitter of beta rays. Since beta rays lose all of their energy within a small fraction of an inch of travel through matter, strontium 90 can damage internal tissues only if it enters the body. Hence it is classed as an internal hazard. Secondly, strontium 90 has a relatively long physical half-life—28 years. This is an important measure of the total dose of radiation that it will deliver. Consider the case of two samples of radioactive material which are similar in all ways except that one isotope has a very short half-life and the other a very long half-life. When placed under a Geiger counter, both samples produce radioactive disintegrations at the rate of 1,000 counts per minute. An hour from now the one with the very short half-life may be down to ten counts per minute, while the one with the long half-life will still yield 1,000 counts per minute— and in truth may still show a disintegration rate of 900 counts per minute some hundreds of years from now. On the basis of total radiation dose delivered over a period of years, obviously the sample with the longer half-life is more dangerous—and the danger is roughly proportional to the half-life.

Next, is strontium 90 readily absorbed in the gastrointestinal tract? The answer is *yes*. In this it differs from many other fallout products. Uranium and plutonium are far more dangerous than strontium 90 and are present in the fallout in higher concentration. The only reason they are not our greatest radiologic hazard today is that they form extremely insoluble chemical compounds which are not readily absorbed from food as it passes through the intestinal tract. The same is true for ruthenium, rhodium, and a number of other major fission products.

Finally, strontium 90 also meets the fourth criterion of danger: it is rapidly concentrated in the skeleton. Some 99 per cent of the total body supply of calcium is contained in the skeleton. When strontium 90 and other bone-seeking elements enter the body, they are likewise concentrated in the skeleton.

The bones are composed of billions of tiny crystals of a complex calcium phosphate salt. Because of their small size and very large number, the crystals in aggregate have a huge total surface area—more than 100 acres in the skeleton of the average man. Body fluids bathing the crystal surfaces bring dissolved minerals to them. There is a constant interchange of minerals between the body fluids and the surface of these crystals. Certain minerals, notably strontium and the heavy metals, are strongly attracted and cling tenaciously to the crystal surfaces. If a crystal is growing or changing its form, the mineral may become trapped inside the crystal; in that case, it will be held for many years. If the mineral happens to be radioactive strontium 90, it acts as a practically permanent focal point of radiation within the bone.

In an adult this type of incorporation is a slow process. Each year a small fraction, perhaps 5 per cent, of the skeletal calcium and other bone mineral constituents move from a surface position to an interior position or vice versa. This comes about by slow physical changes in the bone, with attendant dissolution or partial dissolution of some crystals and formation of some new ones or new surfaces on old ones. Thus the adult can ingest large amounts of radioactive bone-seekers and still have only small amounts of these minerals permanently trapped in his skeleton over the course of years.

In a child the situation is quite different. He is rapidly building a skeleton. From one to five years of age the child increases his skeleton weight by about 20 per cent per year. This situation provides opportunity for a much more rapid incorporation of radioactive materials into bone mineral. Current data show that the strontium 90 concentrations in the skeletons of small children are four to seven times greater than those in their parents. Once the child has become an adult, because of the slow rate of exchange at that stage, it will be extremely slow and difficult to remove this radioactive material—even if a procedure for doing this is discovered.

Strontium 90 and other radioactive materials are not deposited uniformly throughout the skeleton. The result is that some spots are much "hotter" than others. Going from the ribs to the shafts of the long leg bones, we may find as much as a twenty- to thirtyfold difference in the strontium 90 concentration. Studies in Sweden indicated that the "hottest" spots in the skeleton may well be six to 60 times hotter than the skeletal average. Portions of the skeleton laid down before 1950 may be nearly free of strontium 90, whereas recently deposited bone mineral may contain five to 40 strontium units. (A strontium unit is one micromicrocurie strontium 90 per gram of calcium.)

Hot Spots

This brings us to the current debate between what might be called the "averagers" and the "hot spotters." The averaging school of thought has been upheld by the Atomic Energy Commission and the National Committee on Radiation Protection and Measurement (on which the AEC is well represented). They have based their estimates of fallout hazards on *averages* and tended to discount the importance of variations. On this basis the National Committee in 1959 downgraded the strontium 90 hazard and raised the occupational limit from 1,000 strontium units to 2,000.

The "hot spotters," on the other hand, focus upon the points of highest radioactivity as indications of the biological hazard. Understandably they tend to arrive at lower rather than higher strontium 90 tolerance levels. Arne Engstrom, in Sweden, is a leading exponent of the hot spotters' point of view. The International Commission on Radiation Protection took a step in this direction in 1959 by lowering the strontium 90 tolerance threefold to 67 strontium units for the general population—one thirtieth of the occupational limit.

To demonstrate the great difference between the averagers' and hot spotters' points of view, let us consider a specific case: that of a person whose skeleton contains 180 strontium units. If we assumed, with the AEC, that the strontium 90 is uniformly distributed throughout the skeleton, this level would produce an estimated radiation dose to the bone of about one half of one roentgen unit per year—only slightly more than the natural background radiation. Such a dose would seem safe and tolerable by any reasonable standards. But, the hot spotters point out, the initial assumption is not correct. The strontium 90 is not distributed uniformly throughout the skeleton; in fact, there may be spots 60 times hotter than the 180-strontium-unit average—that is to say, spots as hot as 10,000 strontium units or more. Such spots would produce an estimated level of radiation that might cause bone cancer, or at least would be expected to do damage to the bone and to double or triple the chances of contracting leukemia or anemia.

This example serves well to demonstrate why scientists must disagree about the hazard at this time. Depending upon the starting assumptions, one can conclude either that the person in the example is perfectly safe and has no cause for alarm or that he is on the verge of mortal peril. Because bone cancer typically requires 15 to 20 years to develop symptoms, it is unfortunately true that no one will be able to settle the argument with finality before the 1980's.

Meanwhile, what is the course of wisdom? Some claim that where there is honest doubt, public safety demands that the safety standards be adjusted to cover the worst possible contingency. But if one couples Dr. Engstrom's estimate of 100 strontium units as the maximum permissible level for radiation workers with the International Commission's suggestion that the permissible level for a population should be one thirtieth the occupational level, it would appear that the population limit should be only three strontium units. Some children have already passed this mark. The official agencies point out that, in the absence of proof that such a level is in any way deleterious, it would be the height of irresponsibility to raise a public alarm.

So far the "averagers" have dominated the national committees entrusted with the setting of safety standards. Again, one example may suffice. A recent report by the National Committee on Radiation Protection and Measurement defined the population tolerance as 14,000,000 roentgen units per million population per 30 years of radiation to the reproductive cells (on the assumption that genetic effects are the only ones of importance). At first glance this figure looks much the same as the "safe" dose of half of one roentgen unit per person per year —perhaps a little smaller. However, it introduces a dangerous concept: that the *individual* is not important, that only the average exposure per million population needs to be considered.

Substantial areas in Nevada and Utah close to the bomb testing grounds had received ten roentgens of gamma radiation as early as 1955. Some 40 communities had had average doses between one and eight roentgen units. Such doses are substantially above allowable levels for the general population—or for professional personnel, for that matter. But in discussing the hazard in this area at a Congressional hearing, Gordon Dunning of the AEC's Division of Biology and Medicine testified as follows:

> In terms of general populace around the Nevada test site, I had a little problem finding a million people for a general population, but if one mentally makes larger and larger circles until he encompasses a million people, then the average exposure to the one million is one tenth of a roentgen unit for six years of testing, which is at the rate of half a roentgen unit per 30 years, which is one twentieth of the maximum exposures recommended by the two committees.

This line of reasoning suggests that a lethal dose of radiation to several thousand persons would appear "safe" if one averaged this total dose over a population of one million over a period of 30 years! It brings out clearly the danger of relying on average figures.

Summary

In this chapter we have followed the bomb debris from its deposition on the earth to its eventual residence in man. We have seen that the bomb cloud in the first few hours delivers massive doses of penetrating radiation to every living thing in its path, similar in effect to large doses of X-rays to the whole body. More selective and equally serious biological effects may be produced when radioactive materials enter the body with food or drinking water or are inhaled as dust particles. The long-term fallout, coming largely from stratospheric sources, is composed of strontium 90 and other long-lived radioactive products, some of which tend to be concentrated in the skeleton. The concentration of strontium 90 in food materials has been increasing rapidly in the last few years. An individual's intake depends upon a number of factors. One of the most important is the relative proportion of milk and plant products in his diet: the more milk and the less plant material in his diet, the smaller will be the amount of strontium 90 associated with each gram of dietary calcium. There are many problems in trying to evaluate the hazard from strontium 90 in the body. One of the main difficulties is assessing the biological significance of "hot spots." Official tolerance levels have reflected a tendency to ignore this problem. In several cases averages have been used to obscure the wide range of biological variation, and to make doubtful situations appear safe.

4 JOHN M. FOWLER

The Rising Level
of Fallout

When the United States, the U.S.S.R., and Great Britain suspended testing of nuclear weapons in the fall of 1958, they had
detonated a total of 174 megatons—92 megatons of fission explosions and 82 megatons of fusion. Each megaton of fission
produces about 100 pounds of fission products; therefore the
total release of radioactive material amounted to some 9,200
pounds. Most of this decayed within a short time, but it included
roughly 140 pounds of long-lived strontium 90 and a larger
amount of cesium 137. In addition, the fusion explosions probably created some 1,300 pounds of long-lived carbon 14.

A great deal of this material is still floating in the atmosphere,
steadily dripping more contamination upon the soil. Hence even
without any further bomb tests we must expect the radioactivity
of our food to increase in the coming years to considerably
higher levels than any measured so far. How high will it rise?
Let us see what predictions can be made on the basis of present
levels and our estimates of the atmospheric load.

Figure 7 shows the measured levels of strontium 90 in the
soil and in milk at various cities in the United States in 1958.
The soil measurements were made in October, 1958; the milk
samples were measured in the summer of 1958 by the United
States Public Health Service and by Consumers Union.

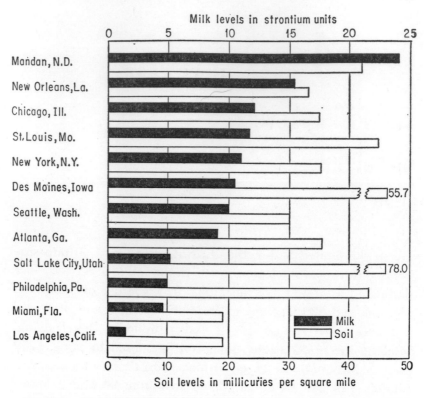

FIG. 7. Local levels of strontium 90 in the soil and in milk at various locations in the
United States in October, 1958.

Obviously the most striking feature of these figures is the wide
variation at the various localities. In the soil, the strontium 90
level ranged from 78 millicuries per square mile at Salt Lake
City down to less than 20 at Los Angeles and Miami (which
fortunately ran a dead heat, providing no ammunition for the
rival Chambers of Commerce). In milk, the variation was even
greater: from more than 23 strontium units at Mandan, N. D.,
down to 1.9 strontium units at Los Angeles. This wide variability from place to place has been confirmed by the systematic
measurements of J. L. Kulp and his associates in Columbia University's Lamont Geophysical Laboratory, who found some milk
samples five times as radioactive as the average. Similarly, a
survey by scientists of the Los Alamos Scientific Laboratory in

1957 showed that milk levels varied from 0.8 of a strontium unit in Arizona to 11.3 strontium units in North Dakota. Many factors are responsible for the variations: differences in latitude, in distance from the test sites, in rainfall, in topography (which affects the runoff of the fallout in cattle feeding ranges), and so on. The chart shows that the strontium level in milk in a given locality is not necessarily related to the level in the soil at that locality, for a city's milk may come from a large milk-shed whose cattle feeds grow in different soils. The soil samples were usually taken at flat, grassy airports; it is not surprising, therefore, that the milk samples, representing much more varied grazing lands, show much greater variability in strontium content.

The world-wide picture of the strontium fallout is shown in Figure 8, which gives the soil strontium 90 levels at a score of representative cities in North and South America, Europe, Asia, and the Pacific. Here the effects of latitude and of rainfall, as discussed in Chapter 2, emerge more clearly. The fallout tends to concentrate most heavily in middle latitudes and in areas of considerable rainfall. We find the highest strontium 90 levels in mid-latitude cities such as New York, Chicago, and Florence, Italy; Hawaii, with the highest level of all, is a special case because it is near the Pacific test sites and has heavy rainfall. Since nearly all the bomb tests have taken place in the Northern Hemisphere, we are not surprised to find less fallout in the Southern Hemisphere. The town of Antofagasta in Chile, where it is said never to have rained, combines all the advantages as a refuge: it has only the barest trace of strontium 90.

Strontium Levels in Our Food and Bones

So much, then, for the strontium levels found in the soil and in milk. What concerns us more is how much gets into our bones. The best measure, of course, would be direct analysis of the bones themselves. Kulp's group at the Lamont Geophysical Laboratory analyzed a number of bone samples collected in

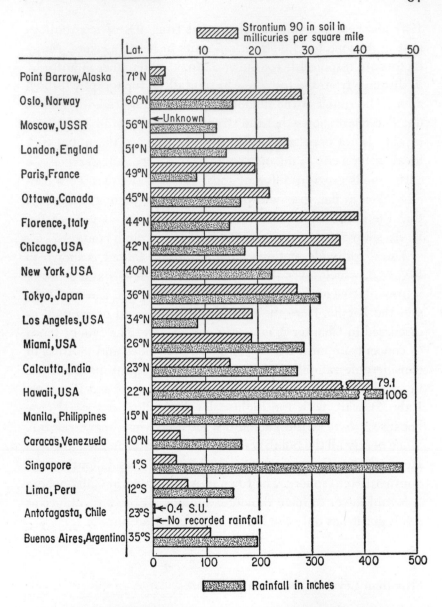

FIG. 8. Strontium 90 in the soil at various locations around the world. The total rainfall from 1953 to 1958 is shown for comparison; at a given latitude, the amount of fallout tends to be related to the amount of rainfall at each location.

the years 1954 to 1958, and they found that the average strontium 90 level in the samples of children's bones in the United
States increased from 0.39 of a strontium unit in 1954–1955 to
1.38 strontium units in 1957–1958. But the number of bone
samples available for analysis was small—only ten in 1954–
1955 and 32 in 1957–1958. The amount of material for study
may be vastly expanded by a project being carried out in St.
Louis under the sponsorship of a group called the Citizens Committee for Nuclear Information. It is collecting the baby teeth
of St. Louis children, with information about whether they were
breast-fed or bottle-fed and where they lived while the teeth
were forming. These deciduous teeth will be ideal indicators of
children's uptake of strontium year by year, because they are
built within one year. The committee hopes to collect 50,000
teeth per year, representing various diets, geographical locations, and so on. This large sample should yield reliable information not only about the general rise in accumulation of
radiostrontium by children but also about the range of individual variation—that is to say, how high the strontium level
may go in individual cases.

For the time being we must attempt to estimate the uptake
of strontium 90 on the basis of the levels in milk and other foods,
as Professor Caster explained in the preceding chapter. Let us
take as a starting point the measurements made in 1958 by the
AEC on the average diet in New York City. These showed that
the average New Yorker got 63 per cent of his dietary calcium
(233 grams) from milk, and other significant amounts from
cereals, fruit and vegetables (see Figure 9). The over-all
strontium 90 concentration in his food was 15 strontium units.
Assuming that the strontium 90 level in foods other than milk
is more or less uniform for the United States (because cereals,
fruits, etc., are transported nationwide), we can estimate the
dietary strontium level in each city from the measured level in
its milk. The results of these computations for cities where
monthly measurements of milk were made in 1958 are shown in
Figure 10. The dietary level ranged from 12.9 strontium units

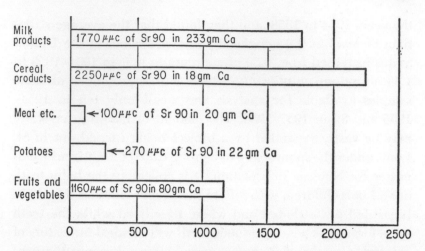

FIG. 9. Amount of strontium 90 in the average diet of New York City residents in 1958. The average consumer got a total of 373 grams of calcium in his food, and the strontium 90 mixed with this calcium amounted to 5,550 micromicrocuries, or 15 strontium units.

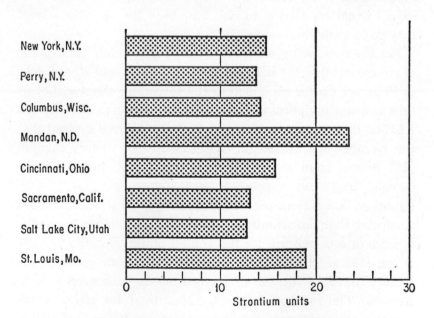

Fig. 10. Strontium 90 concentration in the average diet at various cities in the United States in 1958.

in Salt Lake City to over 23 strontium units in Mandan, N. D. Among the large cities sampled, St. Louis stood highest, with 18.9 strontium units.

A similar analysis of the British diet (milk contributing 53 per cent of the calcium) and the measured strontium contamination (less than in the United States) puts the English dietary level at about seven strontium units in 1958. In Japan, where most of the calcium in the diet comes from rice and other plants and only about 18 per cent from milk, the dietary level of strontium 90 in 1958 is calculated to have been between eight and 40 strontium units, depending on whether white or brown rice was the major calcium source. For the rest of the world we can make only rough estimates based on the percentage of calcium in the diet contributed by milk and milk products; in general, other things being equal, the higher the percentage of calcium contributed by plant sources, the higher the concentration of strontium 90 in the bones; the more calcium contributed by milk, the lower the strontium level, thanks to the cow's "filtration system." The table below shows the relative importance of milk in the diet of various countries:

	Percentage of Calcium in the Diet from Dairy Products		Percentage of Calcium in the Diet from Dairy Products
Argentina	79	Italy	62
Australia	82	Japan	18
Brazil	60	Mexico	56
Canada	85	Netherlands	83
China	23	Norway	86
Finland	84	Philippines	18
France	75	Poland	55
Germany	74	Spain	50
Great Britain	81	Switzerland	87
Greece	63	Thailand	55
India	51	Union of South Africa	71
Indonesia	11	United States	80

Once we have estimated how much strontium 90 a person gets in his food, we can go on to calculate how much he will lay down in his bones. The human system, preferring calcium to strontium, will reject much of the strontium intake and incorporate only from one quarter to one half of it. If we take the proportion to be one quarter, then the average resident of St. Louis, where the dietary level in 1958 was about 20 strontium units, absorbed about five strontium units in his bones. This is considerably higher than the average level actually measured by Kulp in his bone samples from various parts of the country, but several factors could account for the discrepancy; for example, the higher-than-average strontium level in St. Louis milk may be one of the reasons for the difference.

We must also bear in mind, as Professor Caster has pointed out in the preceding chapter, that averages in this context are misleading: we are concerned with the exposure of persons, and some individuals will have far more than the average amount of strontium. Analyzing the 1956 bone measurements statistically, my Washington University colleague W. C. Bauer and I concluded that if these few samples were representative, four children in 1,000 would deposit ten times the average amount of strontium 90 in their bones. Kulp estimated from the 1958 samples that in each age group one per cent of the population may exceed five times the average. He put the limit at 20 times the average, but this seems more an expression of hope than of fact, for his group has already found one bone sample with a radiostrontium level 75 times the average.

The Levels in Prospect

We have considered the quantitative relations between the fall-out deposited on the ground, the amount appearing in people's diets, and the amount finally deposited in their bones. We are now in a position to venture some predictions about what is in store for us in the next few years, though the reader must realize that the predictions are necessarily hedged with many uncertainties.

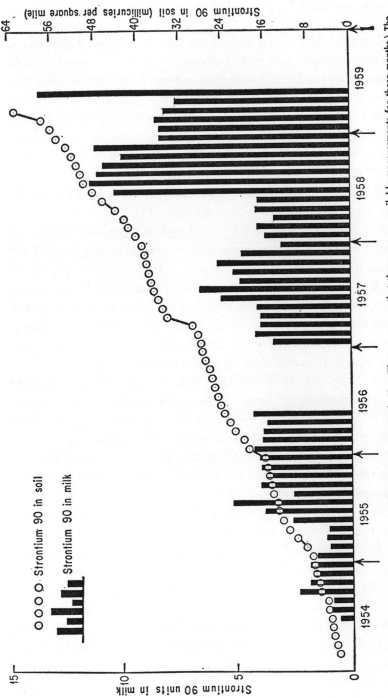

FIG. 11. The rising level of strontium 90 in milk in New York City. (The gaps mean that there are no available measurements for those months.) The accumulation of strontium 90 in the soil is shown for comparison.

We might first take a look at the trend of the past few years. The most careful and systematic study of the accumulation of strontium 90 has been conducted in New York City by scientists in the New York office of the AEC. Since 1954 they have made monthly measurements of the strontium 90 in rainfall (nearly all fallout is brought down in rain) and also frequent measurements of the strontium accumulation in soil and in milk. The fallout of strontium and its accumulation in the soil have risen steadily since 1954; so has the strontium level in milk, allowing for seasonal fluctuations (see Figure 11).

How much strontium 90 is still to fall from the bombs exploded up to 1958? We know that they produced a total of 9.2 megacuries of this fission product. AEC scientists estimated that 3.2 megacuries were out of general circulation by the spring of 1959; that amount had decayed or been deposited in the bomb testing areas. This left six megacuries: about three megacuries were estimated to be in the soil around the world and three megacuries still floating in the stratosphere.

The "drip-out" from the stratosphere will continue to build up the strontium 90 level in the soil for some time to come. The level will rise to a peak and then decline, because of the decay of the isotope. From the information we have about the "drip-out" rate and the rate of decay, we can draw a curve forecasting the likely soil levels in the coming years (assuming no more bomb tests).*

From the predicted strontium levels in the soil, we can estimate the consequent levels in the diet, and from the amount in the diet in turn we can estimate how much will be deposited in people's bones. On the foregoing basis, we have plotted a forecast for the next 20 years at St. Louis, as a typical midwestern city. The results are shown in Figure 12: its three curves represent the predicted strontium levels in the soil, in the diet, and in the bones of children (assuming that one fourth of the

---

* The curve was originally drawn on the assumption that the mean lifetime of fallout in the stratosphere was three years. Later evidence indicates it may be only nine months.

amount in the diet gets into their growing bones). According to our calculations, the peak of the strontium 90 level will come in 1965. The concentration in the soil then will be 108 millicuries per square mile—more than double that in 1958. The average bone dose will be about 11 strontium units—more than twice the estimated average in St. Louis in 1958. After 1965 the levels will gradually decline, but in 1980 they will still be higher than they were in 1958 or 1959.

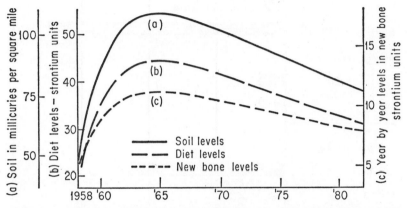

FIG. 12. Predicted future levels of strontium 90 in the soil, in milk, and in children's bones at St. Louis (taken as a typical midwestern city). According to this projection, the contamination from the bomb tests conducted up to 1958 (when testing was suspended) will rise to a peak in 1965 and then gradually decline as the radioactive strontium decays. In the event of a resumption of bomb testing, the curves, of course, will change.

By the same sort of calculation, adapted to typical national diets, we would estimate that in 1965 the average strontium 90 level in children's bones will be 9.3 strontium units in the United States, 4.1 units in Great Britain, and somewhere between five and 25 units in Japan.

More meaningful than the strontium level is the question: How much radiation will we receive from the strontium in our bones in the coming years? Consider a child born in 1958— what will be the total dosage to his vulnerable bone marrow in his lifetime? It is possible to venture an estimate about this, though the calculations are complex and rest upon some uncertain assumptions about the building of bone and other factors. It turns out that the maximum total irradiation of the bone marrow (*i.e.*, at hot spots) may amount to nearly six rem in a 70-year lifetime. (The rem, a unit of radiation dose, is defined in the next chapter.) As Figure 13 shows, this is almost as much

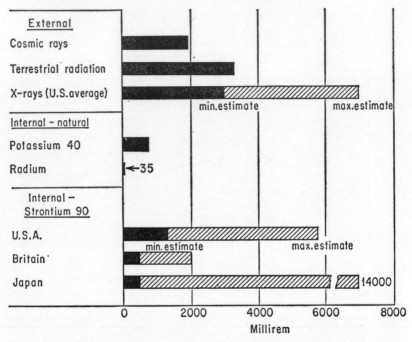

FIG. 13. Lifetime exposure to radiation from natural sources and from strontium 90 in fallout. The exposure is expressed as the total irradiation of the bone marrow (where leukemia and other diseases may be generated) over the next 70 years. Minimum and maximum estimates are given because individual exposures vary widely.

as the lifetime exposure from all natural sources combined— cosmic rays, ground radiation, radium, potassium 40, etc. It is not far behind the estimate of the X-ray exposures that a United States citizen gets during his lifetime. Thus strontium 90 may add half as much radiation as comes from all normal sources to the burden that will be carried by children now being born. And this presupposes that there will be no more bomb tests. If testing continued for the next five years at the rate of the last five, the lifetime dose from strontium 90 would be doubled.

It is only fair to point out that this estimate is extremely tentative and differs considerably from some others. For example, Merril Eisenbud of the AEC has estimated that "the maximum foreseeable dose from strontium 90 in the New York area" will be only "about 5 per cent of the dose due to natural radioactivity." However, his figures were based on the strontium 90 levels in New York City's food, which are lower than those in St. Louis (15 strontium units as against 19); what is much more important, he assumed uniform irradiation of the bone, whereas we must take account of hot-spot radiation at particular points in the bone marrow. Penetrating natural radiation such as cosmic rays irradiates the whole bone evenly, but strontium 90's short-range radiation is apt to concentrate at specific points. Prudence demands that we reckon with these maximum points of exposure, because they may become the focal points of cancer, leukemia, or other biological damage.

Cesium 137

Let us now consider the second most important element in fallout—cesium 137. Like strontium 90, it is a fission product which tends to accumulate in the body and presents a long-range hazard. Many of the considerations that we applied to strontium 90 apply also to cesium 137, and on this basis we can predict the probable bodily levels of cesium.

First we must note some important differences. Cesium 137 does not concentrate in bone or any other single tissue but is distributed throughout the body. Moreover, while it has about the same physical half-life as strontium 90 (30 years), its biological half-life is short: its average stay in the body is only about 17 days. For these reasons the cesium fallout is less important than strontium as far as causing cancer is concerned.

On the other hand, its general distribution through the body and its penetrating radiation (gamma rays are emitted in its decay series) make it dangerous to the genes. In other words, the hazard of cesium 137 is mainly to mankind's heredity.

Cesium resembles potassium chemically and travels with potassium in the body, just as strontium goes into the body as a fellow-traveler with its chemical cousin calcium. In contrast to the strontium case, however, the body seems to *prefer* cesium to potassium, and so the level of cesium in the body is roughly twice that in the diet. The concentration of cesium 137 is measured in terms of micromicrocuries of cesium per gram of potassium. Thus we can speak of "cesium units" in the same sense as strontium units.

The cesium 137 level in the body can be measured rather easily: unlike the short-range beta radiation of strontium 90, which is trapped at the site where the decay takes place, the penetrating gamma radiation of cesium 137 passes through the tissues and can be detected outside the body. There are radiation counters which can measure the cesium 137 radiation emerging from the whole surface of a person's body, as was mentioned in the Introduction. The Los Alamos, Argonne, and Walter Reed Hospital laboratories have this type of counter, and measurements have been made on a number of visitors to these three laboratories. Their average bodily level of cesium 137 has been about 60 "cesium units." The individuals measured may not be representative (it is doubtful, for instance, that the Far Eastern visitors to the laboratories represent the typical diets of the general population of their countries), but the measurements do give some idea of the approximate level of cesium 137 in people's bodies as of 1958.

In attempting to forecast future levels, we can follow the same procedure as we did with strontium 90. To begin with, the total amount of cesium 137 produced by the 92 megatons of fission explosions up to 1958 is believed to have been about 16 to 17 megacuries—more than twice the amount of strontium 90. The amount of cesium in the soil at any given place will therefore probably be about twice the amount of strontium, since the cesium presumably travels with the strontium in the bomb debris. Moreover, cesium, like strontium, comes into our bodies mainly in milk: in the United States diet 60 per cent of the cesium is contributed by milk and 25 per cent by meat (see Figure 14). Wright Langham and E. C. Anderson of Los Alamos

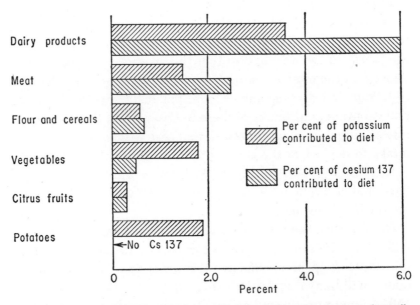

FIG. 14. Radioactive cesium 137 in the average United States diet. Cesium is chemically akin to potassium and travels with it. In this estimate, by Wright Langham and E. C. Anderson, the cesium 137 concentration in the average diet in 1956–1957 was 20 micromicrocuries per gram of potassium.

estimated that the cesium 137 level in the United States diet in 1956–1957 was about 20 micromicrocuries per gram of potassium. According to monthly measurements by the United States Public Health Service at several sampling stations, the average cesium 137 concentration in milk in 1958 was 44 micromicrocuries per gram of potassium (or 44 "cesium units"), against 32 units in 1957.

Assuming that this increase held true for the rest of our diet, the dietary level in 1958 may be estimated at 30 cesium units, and the average concentration in the body would be twice that, or 60 micromicrocuries of cesium 137 per gram of potassium. Here we must note that because of cesium 137's penetrating gamma radiation, we are subjected to radiation not only from the cesium in our bodies but also from that in our external environment—that is, the cesium 137 in the soil and other objects in our surroundings.

From all this information we can project some predictions about our cesium 137 exposure in the coming years. I should point out that these forecasts for cesium, as well as for strontium, are based on the assumption that the amount of exposure will depend on the total *accumulation* of fallout rather than the *rate* of fallout. If leafy vegetables were our main source of cesium and strontium, our intake of these isotopes might depend on the rate of fallout on plant leaves; in that case we should expect the intake to decline in the coming years, because the fallout rate is diminishing. The strontium 90 level in milk, on the other hand, tends to follow the rising accumulation in the soil, not the rate of bomb testing.

Our forecast, then, supposes that the concentration of cesium will follow the same rising curve as that of strontium (see Figure 12); at the peak in 1965 the average cesium 137 level in our bodies will be two and a half times the 1958 average, or about 150 cesium units. Over the next 30 years (the human reproductive span), the total dose of cesium radiation to an American child born in 1958 will average 95 millirem, or about one tenth of one rem; in Great Britain it will be 115 millirem; in Japan, 95 millirem. This is only a small fraction of the radiation from natural sources, but laboratory evidence indicates that even a slight increase in radiation increases the amount of genetic damage.

Carbon 14

This brings us to carbon 14, the third long-lived isotope I mentioned at the beginning of the chapter. How much will this add to the genetic hazard? We estimated that the bomb tests have added 1,300 pounds of carbon 14 to the 1,900 pounds already in the atmosphere from cosmic-ray bombardment. Altogether the earth contains some 80 tons of natural radiocarbon—the one ton in the air, three tons in plant life, and 76 tons in the oceans. In time, most of the bomb-created radiocarbon also will mix into the oceans. Its net addition to the terrestrial total of carbon 14 will be only about one per cent: this means that the radiocarbon from the bomb tests to date will increase the average exposure of a person's sex organs over a 30-year span by only half of one millirem over the 48 millirems already received from natural radiocarbon. One is tempted to ignore this completely, but carbon 14 has a long life (half-life: 5,600 years), and over a period of thousands of years the genetic damage from even this small increase in radiation will take a large toll in the absolute number of persons harmed.

So far we have reviewed the origin, the amount, the distribution, and the human destination of fallout. The next two chapters will examine in some detail the effects of fallout radiations upon living matter.

5 WALTER R. GUILD

Biological Effects of Radiation

Experimental studies of the effects of radiation, particularly in connection with medical uses of X-rays and radium, began soon after the discovery of these radiations. Some of the early work was quackery; in fact, there were "healers" who prescribed "radium water" to treat everything from headaches to hangnails. (More than 100 persons who were subjected to this treatment have been found and are being studied for long-delayed effects; the AEC is looking for others who may have been exposed to radium in those days.)

There was a good deal of sound work in various laboratories, however, and by 1928 an International Commission on Radiation Protection had begun to formulate exposure limits for people working with radiation. Since World War II, of course, research on biological effects of radiation has been expanded greatly. This work is beginning to show practical as well as purely scientific results. It is no longer hopeless, for instance, to expect that something can be done to lessen or even reverse radiation damage, although it is doubtful that such measures could be applied practically on a scale wide enough to deal with fallout.

The ways in which radiation damages living things are being studied from two opposite approaches: on the one hand, by irradiating a whole animal, and on the other, by irradiating single cells and even parts of cells (*e.g.*, specific proteins) to find out what makes the whole animal sick. The connection between these is beginning to be filled in.

Acute Effects

Consider an experiment in which 200 rats are exposed to X-rays. What happens to them depends on many factors—the size of the dose, how many times it is repeated, the time between repeats, whether the whole body or only part of it is exposed, the kind of treatment given after the X-ray.

When the dose is large enough and given in a relatively short time, the rats will become acutely sick within a few days and may die within a month. Those that do not die will recover what seems to be reasonable health, but soon or late they will have various troubles. They may be scrawny or may show odd-colored patches of hair. Some will finally die of a cancer. And the average life span of the surviving group will be shorter than if they had not been irradiated.

Heavy doses, therefore, put an acute load on the body and also produce a longer-term damage. It is possible to recover from the acute effect, and in this sense "radiation damage" is reversible. In fact, one can now treat animals so as to increase greatly the chance of recovering from the acute effects. Much effort is going to see whether such treatments will reduce the long-term effects: so far the results say *No* (see Chapter 8).

Several specific kinds of acute radiation death are known, mainly from work with small animals. When the whole body receives a dose in the range of 300 to 800 roentgens, the small intestine gives trouble within a few days: there is severe nausea and weakness, and the lining of the intestine almost sloughs off, exposing the animal to heavy loss of fluids and peritonitis (infection in the abdominal cavity). The intestine usually recovers, and in a few more days the patient feels better. But after two to three weeks the blood-forming system gives out: the bone marrow stops producing cells, and the patient usually dies. This is called "marrow death." In the case of human beings, a dose of 600 roentgens is sufficient to cause marrow death for almost everyone exposed; 400 to 500 roentgens will kill about half of those exposed; and 300 roentgens will kill only a few.

Injections of bone-marrow cells taken from an unirradiated donor can protect against doses perhaps two to three times as high as these. Or shielding even a single leg or arm bone from the radiation will greatly improve an animal's chances of recovery. It seems that a few surviving marrow cells are all it takes to repopulate the marrow and prevent the acute death. Marrow injections were successfully applied to victims of a reactor accident in Yugoslavia in 1958 (see Chapter 7).

When the dose is 1,000 roentgens or more, marrow injections cannot help. The small intestine fails to recover from its early damage, and the patient dies about one week after exposure. This outcome, characteristic of irradiation in the range somewhat above 1,000 r (roentgens), is called "intestinal death."

At much higher doses—somewhere above 3,000 r—comes what is called "central nervous system death." The nerve tissue is comparatively resistant and shows no sign of damage up to these doses, but at this level it succumbs abruptly. Apparently the nerve cells' ability to discriminate between sodium and potassium suddenly breaks down, and the patient dies within a few hours or a day or two after the exposure.

The three AEC employees who have been killed in radiation accidents suffered these three kinds of death. One was exposed to 800 to 900 r and succumbed to marrow death in 26 days; another had 1,900 r and intestinal death in nine days; the third, 12,000 r and central nervous system death in 36 hours.

At much lower levels of exposure, we can still see some acute effects. Local irradiation of just the hands, the jaw, or some other organ may produce a burn, loss of hair, temporary sterility, or a dry skin. A dose of 50 to 100 r to a large portion of the body may cause temporary effects on the blood, though the person may not feel ill at all.

Finally we come to the milder doses which show no immediate symptoms but are still of concern to practicing radiologists, to people occupationally exposed, and to all of us because of our lifelong exposure to background radiation, X-rays, and now fallout. The long-term effects of these small doses are the same as those that show up after recovery from acute exposures. There are three main kinds: genetic damage, cancer, and shortening of life.

An important point is that the tolerance to a given dose of radiation is increased if the dose is spread out over a period of time. This applies even to heavy doses. Thus the late Egon Lorenz at the National Cancer Institute found that when a colony of mice was exposed to 8.8 roentgens per day, 50 per cent of the colony survived for 18 months and took a total accumulated dose of 4,700 roentgens, nearly eight times the lethal dose for a single exposure. In another experiment in which the dose was split over just two days, it took 1,000 roentgens to kill 50 per cent of a group of rats that would have been killed by a single dose of 750 roentgens; that is, after a dose of 375 r the first day, it took 625 r more the second day to kill half the rats. All this implies that there is a certain rate of recovery between doses.

Fractionating the dose appears to reduce long-term effects also—e.g., the induction of cancer and shortening of life. We have no reliable data yet on just how great the reduction is for these effects, but it appears to be at least a factor of two or three. We must bear this in mind when we try to estimate the damage done by fallout. The damage is probably less than experiments with single exposures would indicate.

Is There a Threshold?

We come now to the central problem in the controversy over fallout: Is there a "threshold" dose below which there will be no effect at all? It is clear that a certain minimum dose is required to produce acute illness or death. On the other hand, most authorities agree that there is no threshold for genetic damage: any dose, however small, will take some toll of the genes. The major argument has been whether a threshold exists for the other long-term hazards, particularly cancer. A second question, not always clearly stated, is whether there is a dose *rate* at which we recover from the damage as fast as it accumulates. For acute effects there clearly is such a rate, and we have just noted that some of the delayed effects are reduced when the dose rate goes down. The key question, then, is how far can they be reduced: Will they go to zero or just to a definite small amount?

The answers to this question are not all in yet. It seems at present, however, that the best explanation of the observed facts so far is that there are two kinds of injury—a recoverable and a nonrecoverable part. Recovery in turn has at least two mechanisms—replacement of damaged cells by new ones, and actual recovery of injured cells.

A very significant result, related to this recovery, has been found in genetics, where it was firmly believed not to exist as late as 1957. W. L. Russell, L. B. Russell, and E. M. Kelly at the Oak Ridge National Laboratory found that when the cells of mice were irradiated in an early stage of development, the number of mutations depended in part on the *rate* of dosage, not solely on the total dose. Again, this result seems to fit the idea of cellular recovery of part of the damage, the degree of recovery depending on the dose rate. A part of the damage is definitely nonrecoverable, however, so there is no true threshold. Furthermore, this finding does not invalidate the earlier conclusion that the number of mutations is proportional to the total dose. It merely means that the size of this constant proportion may increase somewhat as the dose *rate* goes up.

We have been considering so far the effects caused by radiation coming from outside the body. The situation becomes more complex when we study radiations from materials *inside* the body, such as the radioactive products in fallout—strontium, cesium, barium, iodine, and so on. The factors of importance in assessing this type of hazard include the physical half-life of the isotope, the nature and range of its radiation, the amount taken up by the body, the duration of its stay, the organ that receives the radiation, and so on.

Some kinds of radiation are more damaging to living tissues than others. For example, alpha particles produce more effect, per unit of dose, than X-rays do. We can rate the various radiations on a scale of "relative biological efficiency" (RBE). Unfortunately for our convenience in standardizing the scale, the RBE of a given radiation may vary with the biological effect being studied. But in general we find that alpha particles have the greatest effect, neutrons come next, and beta particles and X-rays have the lowest efficiency. Alpha particles have a maximum RBE about five times that of X-rays, and fast neutrons have RBE's of about two to two and a half (for typical kinds of damage).

Physically the RBE depends on the distribution of the ions produced by the particle along its track through tissue. The particle creates ions by removing electrons from atoms in its path. A very fast particle, such as a beta particle, scatters ionizations randomly and comparatively widely separated in space, whereas a slower one, such as an alpha particle, makes a dense line of ions along its path. The ions cause damage by disrupting key molecules and structures in the cell, and the efficiency of this damage depends on the way in which they are spread in the cell. The greatest biological damage results from the moderately dense ionization produced by alpha particles of five Mev.

The RBE is now used as the basis for translating the amount of radiation into biologically effective dosage. The unit employed to measure a dose in biological terms (and to express the "maximum permissible exposure") is the rem: it is calculated by multiplying the RBE by the "rad"—a general unit of radiation energy which is very close to the roentgen, long used as the standard for measuring X-rays.

Effects on Individual Cells

It is clear that the damage done by radiation involves both immediate effects on the cells and more remote effects arising from interaction between the cells and the responses of the whole organism to the cellular damage. Much study has therefore gone into the specific effects of radiation on cells. One of the earliest observations was made in 1906, when J. Bergonie and L. Tribondeau in France found that rapidly dividing cells were most sensitive to radiation. The radiation stops the cell from going into mitosis—the process of separating its chromosomes into two sets and forming new cells. After some time the cell may recover and go on dividing. The recovery seems to be complete in some cases, but often the cells suffer a delayed death after dividing for a while.

Experiments to see what happens to cells may be done by irradiating a tissue, such as the root tip of a plant, or by irradiating an animal and examining just a section of tissue, such as the small intestine. There is also a good deal of work now on tissue cultures of animal or plant cells and on single-celled organisms, such as bacteria, where it is easy to get measurements of the killing effect of given doses of radiation and to study the effects of various treatments. Similarly, experiments have been done on single eggs of small insects, where one can arrange to irradiate just the cytoplasm or the nucleus of the egg. In this way Robert C. Von Borstel of Oak Ridge demonstrated very neatly that the nucleus, containing the chromosomes and the genes, is by far the most sensitive part of the cell. It takes only a tiny dose to the nucleus (one or a few alpha particles) to kill the cell, but the cell will survive doses more than 20 times as great when only the cytoplasm is irradiated.

In a typical experiment with bacteria, the culture is allowed to grow until the bacteria reach a certain concentration—say 300,000,000 cells per cubic centimeter—and they are then spun out of the growth liquid in a centrifuge and replanted in a fresh salt solution of known composition. Samples of this suspension are now exposed to a series of X-ray doses, ranging perhaps from 500 to 50,000 roentgens. After their irradiation they are spread out on a gel growth medium in a series of petri dishes. Each cell capable of dividing sufficiently to form a visible "colony" (*i.e.,* 20 to 30 divisions) is counted as a "survivor." The proportion of survivors gives a very accurate measure of the sensitivity of the bacteria to the given radiation. The technique also makes it possible to study the response of the cells to various treatments given after the irradiation.

It is very common to find that the number of surviving bacteria goes down logarithmically with the increase in dose. This is the same kind of relation as the decay of a radioactive source with time, and it implies that each added unit of dose kills a certain *fraction* of the cells still surviving. For example, if 50 per cent of the cells survive 2,000 r, half of these survivors (*i.e.,* 25 per cent of the original group) will survive 4,000 r.

This relationship suggests that the process of killing is a random one, and that a cell survives unless by chance a single event produced by the radiation happens to occur in a "sensitive volume." It is tempting to conclude that the crucial event is an ionization and the "sensitive volume" is a definite structure in the cell. This was the prevailing interpretation in the 1930's, and it was thought that the sensitive structure or "target" in the cell was unvaryingly vulnerable, regardless of variations in temperature, pressure, chemical surroundings, or other external conditions.

Soon, however, it became obvious that this was not so. One could change the sensitivity of bacteria by adding various "protective agents," by changing the amount of oxygen present, and so on. Investigators then shifted to the view that radiation acted indirectly; that is, by chemical action on the water in the cells it produced various "poisons" (*e.g.,* free radicals). The protective agents capable of reducing the sensitivity of the cells were believed to sop up these poisons.

Further experiments are now leading to a somewhat modified view. It turns out that there is a limit to the amount of protection the protective agents can give: no matter how much is added, they cannot reduce the cell's sensitivity by a factor of more than two or three. Moreover, the sensitivity of the cell is strongly influenced not only by the agents or conditions present during the irradiation but also by the previous and subsequent conditions. The kind of nutrients furnished, the temperature at which the cells are held, and numerous special chemical treatments can alter the number surviving a given dose by as much as a hundredfold.

In one set of recent experiments two British workers, Neal Gillies and Tikvah Alper, were able to raise the survival of irradiated bacteria from less than one per cent to the startling figure of better than 50 per cent by treating them with an antibiotic (chloramphenicol). This chemical blocks the cells from synthesizing protein until after they have synthesized some deoxyribonucleic acid (DNA)—the material of which genes are made.

Numerous other experiments show that various metabolic factors determine how much damage will result from a given dose of radiation. It now seems probable that direct and indirect effects both play their part. There is clearly an interaction of at least two factors—the initial damage produced by the radiation on a key part of the cell, and other processes which tend to repair the damage, by-pass it in some way, or leave it to kill the cell or produce a mutation. There seems to be always a residual part of the damage which is not repairable, however.

At an average killing dose a bacterium receives damage in at least ten genes, and a human cell in at least 500. If it is true that a repairing process takes place, these genes seem likely candidates for the repair. One current hypothesis holds that the net damage to the cells can be traced to those few altered genes that fail to be adequately repaired or by-passed by the cell in its normal processes.

A dose of about 50 roentgens will produce an average of about one break in each cell's chromosomes, the structures that carry the genes. The net effect of these breaks is that parts of chromosomes are lost, are shifted about, or stick together so that normal cell division cannot take place. A great deal of work has been and is being done on these chromosome aberrations, and there seems little question that they play an important role in cell damage. Sheldon Wolff of Oak Ridge is finding that here also various treatments given before, during, or after irradiation can modify the final effects. One form of repair depends on the synthesis of protein by the cell. Again, not all of the damage is repairable—as in other effects both at the cellular and the whole animal level, there is a recoverable and a nonrecoverable damage.

Even a very large dose of radiation does not produce any immediate effect on a cell's ordinary metabolic processes, such as the rate of synthesis of protein or the consumption of oxygen and food. For example, after a dose of 60,000 r, a culture of bacteria will go on consuming oxygen at a normal rate for more than an hour, although eventually the cells die, of course. In other words, the immediate effect is not on the respiratory process as such but on something else.

To sum up, our ideas of how radiation kills a cell or produces a mutation are changing as we get more information. On the basis of the early all-or-nothing ideas, we would have concluded no treatment could alter a cell's chances of survival on irradiation. Then we found that treatment during irradiation could protect to some extent, and now even after the irradiation we can do things to alter the final result, as far as a single cell is concerned. Perhaps the most significant new finding is that there are natural repair processes which undo some of the damage from radiation. The residual damage does not drop to zero, even at low-dose rates, but it may be less than was thought.

The Cancer Effect

The most difficult thing to determine is how effective fallout will be in producing cancer. Research in this area is particularly uncertain first because we do not yet know what mechanism makes cells cancerous and secondly because there are many difficulties in interpreting the results of cancer-inducing experiments.

It is certain that radiation can cause cancers. Skin cancers were the earliest seen. Then as high-energy X-ray machines with more penetrating radiations were used, they were found to produce numerous forms of deeper cancers. Further evidence came when it was discovered that nearly half of the German miners digging pitchblende (the ore of radium) in Schneeberg and Joachimstal died of lung cancer. They had been working in an atmosphere containing 30 or more times the present permissible limit of radon. The point was driven home more dramatically by the case of the radium watch-dial painters, some of whom developed bone tumors. More recently experiments on animals have demonstrated that bone cancer can be produced by X-rays or by feeding or injecting various radioactive substances, including strontium 90. In man, the greatest amount of quantitative evidence is for production of leukemia, and most analyses so far have been concerned with this disease, although it is not certain that it is typical of other types of cancer.

The two greatest difficulties in studying the cancer problem are that the effects of low doses tend to be obscured statistically by the spontaneous background rate of cancer incidence and that a considerable time may elapse between exposure and development of a visible cancer. This "latent period" seems to vary from one type of cancer to another. In the case of the German miners, the average period from first exposure to development of cancer was about 17 years. In other series studied, the period has ranged from a year or less to more than 25 years.

For a long time it was thought that repeated exposures were necessary to induce a tumor, and this complicated the definition of latent period. There is now clear evidence from the Hiroshima survivors and from laboratory experiments that a single exposure will suffice. A latent period can then be determined for each individual case. At Hiroshima, leukemia cases were found within two years after the bomb drop; they have continued to accumulate every year since.

In some animal experiments the number of tumors rises to a peak at a certain time after the irradiation and declines thereafter. Likewise, among the people who were exposed to radium poisoning two or three decades ago the number of new bone tumors seems to be declining. More will be known about this in a year or two when the results of the current search for radium-exposure cases are in.

In animal experiments it is frequently observed that the latent period shortens, and the total number of tumors increases, with higher doses of radiation. On the other hand, there have been cases where the incidence of a given cancer *decreased* with radiation exposure, although those tumors that did arise came sooner than without radiation. At first glance this result appears very startling. But it may be explainable by complicating factors. For instance, it is known that a moderate dose of radiation will lengthen the life span of certain strains of female mice, apparently because the dose reduces the number and size of their litters and thus lessens the strain of motherhood. Higher doses do shorten the life span of these mice.

We can arrive at these clear conclusions about radiation and cancer: radiation does increase the incidence of most types of cancer, and the higher the dose, the sooner the cancer appears. At high doses, however, the animal may die of other causes before cancer has had a chance to develop, and so the cancer-inducing effect is obscured.

As to whether there is a threshold dose below which there is no danger, the answer is by no means clear. The most extensive data are those on leukemia. In 1957 E. B. Lewis of the California Institute of Technology analyzed the incidence of leukemia in four groups of people: (1) survivors of the atomic bombs in Japan, (2) children who had been treated with X-rays for enlargement of the thymus gland, (3) adults who had been irradiated for ankylosing spondylitis (a back disease), and (4) radiologists. He found that in general the chances of contracting leukemia seemed to have a linear (*i.e.*, direct) relation to the amount of exposure, down to low doses. He calculated that the leukemia rate would be about two cases per year per million population for each rem of exposure. The most interesting statistic, from the standpoint of the threshold question, was the appearance of six cases among Japanese who had been about a mile from the bomb explosions and were estimated to have received small doses somewhere between 14 and 100 rem. This low figure, together with the general straight-line proportionality between the dosage and leukemia rates, might mean that there is no threshold. However, the actual dose received by the persons a mile from the bomb bursts may have been as high as 100 rem, and some investigators have held that the existence of a threshold at about 100 rem is therefore possible. In any case, the data compiled by Lewis in 1957 certainly did not rule out the possibility of a threshold somewhere below 20 rem—the dose range we are most concerned about when we consider fallout, medical X-rays, and normal exposures.

At least two recent studies tend to bear out Lewis's view that there is no threshold for cancer. One is a further follow-up of Japanese leukemia cases, with more accurate information on exposure, which is reported to show a straight-line relation between dosage and leukemia-induction down to nearly zero. The other is a study by Alice Stewart of children who died of leukemia or other cancers in England and Wales during the years 1953 to 1955. She looked at the radiation history of the mothers of these children during their pregnancy, and she found that there was a strong correlation between X-ray examination of the mother's pelvis during late pregnancy and the probability of the child's developing a malignant disease. The dose to the fetus in such examinations is between two and five roentgens, and this dose appears to have about doubled the child's chance of contracting cancer—mainly leukemia. Other studies in the United States are showing similar results.

There is growing evidence that children are more susceptible to damage in the womb than after birth. This is quite possibly related to the facts that rapidly dividing cells are especially sensitive and that any slight damage to the rapidly developing fetus can disorganize its metabolism and injure the structures it is building at the time of irradiation.

In considering whether there is a threshold for cancers in general, we must bear in mind that leukemia, a blood disease in which white blood cells multiply very rapidly, may not be typical of other cancers. On the whole, we are in the highly unsatisfactory position of being unable to say with any confidence, either from animal experiments or from actual human cases, whether or not there is a threshold for most forms of cancer.

Can we get any further light by considering the theories about how radiation induces cancer? The most widely discussed theory is the "somatic mutation" one. This in its simplest form says that a somatic cell (any cell but a reproductive cell) is changed by radiation in such a way that it turns wild, grows unrestrainedly, and is therefore cancerous. If that is true, any dose, however small, can initiate a cancer. The chief attraction of this hypothesis is its simplicity. But Austin Brues of the Argonne National Laboratory has raised a most interesting argument against it. Man has about 1,000 times as many cells as the mouse, and he lives 30 times longer; on the cell mutation theory one would therefore expect many more cancers in man. Yet the actual cancer rates in man and mouse are not greatly different. Moreover, if a single cell mutation can result in leukemia, there should be a great deal more leukemia than we actually see, judging by the known rate of mutation produced by radiation in experiments on germ cells. The expected and actual rates of leukemia do fall into agreement if we suppose that leukemia is due to a recessive mutation, and that two genes of the same type must be hit to induce it. But if such a double mutation is required, the incidence of leukemia must be proportional to the *square* of the dose, which means that there is a threshold, or at least a nonlinear relation between the dose and the disease.

Other theories of carcinogenesis favor the idea that more than one factor is operating; that is, radiation can induce cells to become potential cancers but a second agent is needed to make them actually cancerous. The agent could be a chemical, a disordered tissue, more radiation, a lack of oxygen, and so on. (It is well known that a continually irritated tissue is likely to turn cancerous.) If this is indeed the case, one should find a threshold in experiments, because it would take a certain amount of radiation to trigger the effect wherever other triggering agents were not present.

At this point one asks what we mean by a linear effect. Let us suppose that radiation induces a cell to be potentially cancerous, and that later by chance—if not sooner by radiation—the second requirement is furnished. If this second requirement is likely to appear anyhow as the person ages, then is the radiation effect linear or not? The answer to this would appear to be that, if the second agent does appear spontaneously within the individual's lifetime, the observed result should then be a linear one. If it appears only sometimes, and more radiation increases its chance of appearing, then one will see a nonlinear relation between the size of dose and the response.

To try to summarize the situation, there is no question that radiation can induce cancers of many types. Both the linear idea and the threshold idea have reasonable theoretical support, though the linear theory has some formidable obstacles to overcome. The data observed in animal experiments seem more consistent with a threshold relationship, but they are not conclusive on this score, and against the animal findings stand the recent data from Japan and from England on human patients, which imply that there is no threshold for leukemia down to two roentgens.

Life-Shortening

Now let us look at the effect of radiation in shortening life—that is, reducing life expectancy in a general way without reference to any particular cause of death.

The most revealing method of analyzing this phenomenon is in terms of the so-called Gompertz function, first used in the early 1800's by Benjamin Gompertz, an English mathematician and actuary, to analyze death rates. One studies the "age-specific death rate," which is the number of deaths per thousand of population at a given age, as it varies with age. Hardin Jones, of the University of California, has used this relation to study many kinds of influence on death rates, from radiation to smoking or overweight. Figure 15 presents some simplified curves which show the general character of the effect of radiation over the life span.

The normal average death rate is fairly high in the early childhood years, dips to its lowest point in the teens and then rises

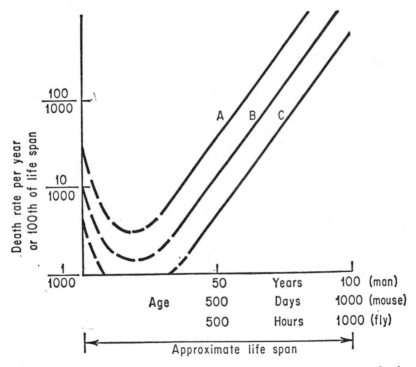

FIG. 15. Gompertz curve of death rates at various ages. Curve B is the average for the total United States population. A deleterious influence, such as radiation or smoking, shifts the normal curve to the left (e.g., from B to A), so that the average life expectancy for the exposed population is shorter at every age.

steadily with advancing age. After the age of 30 or so, the death rate increases at a phenomenally regular pace, doubling about every seven or eight years. This general picture applies not only to human populations but also to other animals, as the figure shows.

Now the most notable feature of the situation is that the form of the curve does not change for different populations: it may shift to one side or the other of the norm (here taken as the middle curve, representing the general average in the United States), but it keeps almost exactly the same slope and shape for every population. That is to say, although one population may have a higher death rate than another, it maintains the same differential throughout the life span, because the decline of viability advances at the same rate everywhere. Jones calls these curves measures of "physiologic age."

The effect of a general influence on health is reflected by a shift of the whole curve toward lower or higher age. For example, pack-a-day cigarette smokers fall on a curve seven years to the left of that for nonsmokers—but with a slope still about the same. Rural dwellers have an advantage of more than five years over city dwellers; women have three years over men, and so on.

A second important feature is that no one cause of death stands out for any population: it appears that the factor at work is the degenerative group of diseases, all of which are increased in likelihood by any past health experiences.

In a 1951 bomb test in the Pacific about 3,000 mice were exposed to varying doses from the explosion. They were then followed until all had died, three to four years later, and detailed autopsies were performed at death. Analysis of their death rates by age showed the same pattern we have been discussing: the radiation exposure had shifted the curve to the left, just as other deleterious influences do. The amount of shift increased with dose. Jacob Furth of the Harvard Medical School and George Sacher of Argonne, who were in charge of the experiments, have analyzed the results in a slightly different fashion from Jones, but they agree on the general outcome. When extrapolated to man, the results say that doses up to 300 to 400 r will shorten life by between four and nine days per roentgen of exposure.

Other experiments generally have been in line with these results. Radiation definitely ages the population so that it dies off from all causes at earlier ages than it otherwise would. And there seems to be no dose threshold for the life-shortening effect.

Some other aspects of this problem have been established. The effect per roentgen is reduced—as much as three times—when the dose is spread out over a long period, as fallout is. On the other hand, the aging effect apparently is not diminished by those protective measures (e.g., injection of spleen or bone-marrow extracts) that are effective in counteracting acute damage.

The doses in these experiments were to the whole body. What will happen when only part of the body is irradiated? This question is now being studied, and it appears that the effect on longevity will depend greatly on what parts of the body are exposed. More data will be forthcoming soon from groups at Argonne, Los Alamos, and elsewhere, but they are not yet available in sufficient detail to draw conclusions.

In at least two experiments on the effects of low doses, mice receiving a dose of about one tenth of a roentgen per day lived longer on the average than control mice which received no radiation! This was first observed by Lorenz and his colleagues during World War II and was so startling that it was repeated after the war and found again. No one has yet given a reasonable explanation of the apparent paradox. It has been suggested that the low-dose radiation may reduce infections in the mouse colony, but that has not been proved. I cite these cases merely as another example of the complexity of the problems in the study of radiation effects; I must quickly add that, because the death rate increases steeply with increasing dose in these experiments, and because even with only a tenth of a roentgen per day mice get more than the normal number of cancers, no serious worker has concluded that a small daily dose is good for you.

Russell at Oak Ridge conducted a very significant experiment which suggests that the mechanism of life-shortening is related to genetic or chromosomal damage. He found that the life-shortening effect carried over to the first-generation offspring of irradiated fathers.

"Permissible Limits"

What can we conclude from all this about "safe" limits of exposure? Our notions of the "maximum permissible exposure" hark back to the early days when little information was available on effects of small doses and when far fewer people were being exposed to radiation than now are. By 1928, after it had become clear that safety standards needed to be set, most groups placed the limit of exposure at 0.1 to 1 roentgen as a maximum daily dose. In 1934 the International Commission on Radiation Protection formally recommended two tenths of a roentgen per day as the limit. The next year our National Committee on Radiation Protection lowered this to one tenth of a roentgen, although the change was mostly a technicality having to do with where and how the dose was measured (air *vs.* tissue).

At about this time the permissible radium level inside the human body was set at one tenth of a microgram. This was based on studies of fewer than 50 cases—radium-dial painters and patients treated medically. In these cases no evidence of bone damage was found in persons with less than 1.2 micrograms of radium; the 0.1 microgram standard was therefore thought to allow a safety factor of at least 12. Since then studies of more persons (still less than 100) have shown some detectable damage at 0.4 of a microgram. This reduces the estimate of the safety factor, but there is now more confidence in it.

In contrast to the radium limit, the allowed limit for exposure to external X-rays was based not on definite information but on "the general impression among radiologists" that exposure of the whole body to a tenth of a roentgen per day produced no harmful effects. It was reassuring to find on calculation that the permitted internal radium dose and the permitted external X-ray exposure actually amounted to about the same thing. That is, one tenth of a microgram of radium in the skeleton is estimated to deliver a biologically effective dose of between 15 and 50 rem per year, while one tenth of a roentgen of X-rays per day corresponds to about 30 rem per year.

In 1947, after data from the Manhattan Project became available, the National Committee (NCRP) lowered the permissible external exposure by about half, to 0.3 rem per week, or about 15 rem per year. This was influenced partly by Lorenz's finding that 0.1 roentgen per day influenced the aging and tumor incidence of mice. In all of these considerations, however, no allowance was made for genetic factors, because it was not considered important in view of the small fraction of the total population exposed.

In 1953 the NCRP listed "maximum permissible concentrations" for about 100 isotopes, generally calculated as that quantity which would deliver 0.3 rem per week to the organ with the highest concentration of the isotope. For strontium 90 the maximum dose for people occupationally exposed was set at one microcurie; this was considered a very conservative dosage, delivering only about 0.036 rem per week to bone—much less than the estimated radiation from the permitted dose of radium.

In 1956, considering the greater number of people exposed, and therefore allowing for some genetic hazard, the International Commission recommended reducing the external exposure limit to one third—that is, to 0.1 rem per week. In the spring of 1959 it revised the internal limits in line with this figure. In the process, the occupational limit for strontium 90 was raised to two microcuries—i.e., about 0.07 rem per week. This action has aroused considerable protest among those concerned with fallout. However, one can note that it does bring strontium 90 into line with the estimates of the risks from other isotopes, and as long as one accepts the premises of a permissible dose at all, it is entirely justified on physical grounds.

All through the history of the ICRP and the NCRP, their main concern has been protection of the relatively small numbers of persons occupationally exposed to radiation. The NCRP has defined "permissible dose" for workers with radiation as "the dose of ionizing radiation that, in the light of present knowledge, is not expected to cause appreciable bodily injury to a person at any time during his lifetime." Considering other occupational risks and the benefits gained from uses of radiation, the standards set for the protection of those who choose to work with radiation appear entirely acceptable as occupational risks.

But "nonoccupational exposure," that is, for the general populace, is another matter. In 1953 the ICRP suggested that one tenth of the occupational exposure level should be acceptable for the general population. When we come to consider acceptability for this area, however, several new questions arise. What do we mean by the indefinite terms "expected" and "appreciable bodily injury"? Is there a threshold for radiation effects, and if not, just how small or large is the risk from fallout? Supposing that there is some risk, what benefits is the general populace receiving that counterbalance the risk?

Estimates of the Risks

To give numbers on how many persons will be hurt by fallout from weapons tests, we must use many assumptions and calculations, all based on rather skimpy data. The results are therefore somewhat uncertain, but they are clear enough to allow this definite conclusion: The number of people hurt will not be zero, and it will also not be so large that each of us has to be anxious about his own personal safety. This will be true even if the number rises to twice or five times the present estimate.

The major risks now foreseeable are those I have mentioned: genetic, cancer, and life-shortening. The chief sources of danger are strontium 90 in the bones, iodine 131 in the thyroid glands, cesium 137 and a few other isotopes in the whole body, and external gamma radiation from recent fallout. I shall try to estimate the possible damage of the population in terms of cancer and life-shortening; in the next chapter Dr. Crow will discuss the genetic risks, which can be taken as the least possible total amount of human damage.

If there is a threshold for the nongenetic forms of damage, then very few people will be hurt directly by the fallout. It seems probable, however, that there is no threshold for leukemia, and perhaps none for life-shortening. For leukemia the main risk comes from strontium 90 irradiating the red bone marrow. Taking the estimated dose to the marrow per strontium unit (0.0006 to 0.001 rem per year), and Lewis's estimate that each rem produces two cases of leukemia per year per million of population, we now have to estimate the number of years over which to add up the exposure. The United Nations committee used 15 years; Lewis, 30 years. These figures then give a range from two to six cases per year per 100 million population per strontium unit in bone. If we suppose that the average strontium 90 concentration in the bones of the United States population will eventually reach ten strontium units (barring further bomb tests), the number of leukemia cases might run as high as 60 per year per 100 million population. But allowing for the probability that much of the population will have a lower level of strontium 90 and for the mitigating effect of the spreadout of the dosage over a period, and striking a mean for the estimates of damage, our best guess is that there will be 40 cases per year for the next 30 to 50 years, or a total of 1,200 to 2,000 cases in the United States population of about 200 million. In the world, the leukemia total might reach 20,000 cases at the same average level of radiation (ten strontium units in the skeleton).

Let us look at this number another way. What is the risk per person with ten strontium units in his bones? Over 70 years his chances of contracting leukemia because of this exposure are in the neighborhood of 4 to 40 in a million.

We have very little basis for estimating the probability of other forms of cancer, but most likely all other cancers together will total less than the number of cases of leukemia.

In trying to estimate the life-shortening effect, the chief problem is to decide what form of dosage and what time scale to use as the measure of effectiveness. Is it the average dose to the whole body or the dose to the bone marrow that is most responsible for general life-shortening? Let us take the worst view, for the purpose of finding the outside limit of the life-shortening effect, and base our calculations on irradiation of the bone marrow by ten strontium units over a whole lifetime of 70 years. The total lifetime dose, then, is between four tenths and seven tenths of a rem, on the average.

According to our best estimates, as we have seen, radiation to the whole body may shorten life by four to nine days per rem. Assuming that there is no threshold, the average shortening of life would amount at most to about six days (0.7 x 9). If we take the lowest figures and allow for the likelihood that there is some repair of the damage from radiation, the shortening of life may be as little as half a day. If there is a threshold, or if marrow dose is not the key to life-shortening, the average loss may be less than half a day.

This small loss is negligible when we compare it with the seven years said to be lost by pack-a-day smokers. But the cigarette smoker has a choice, whereas there is no escape from fallout. And for the whole world population the number is not negligible. Shortening of life by one day as a world average would mean three billion man-days lost. This would amount to more than ten times the loss due to leukemia, if we assume that the lifetime of the 20,000 leukemia victims will be shortened by an average of about 30 years. Indeed, in aggregate man-days of life lost, and in the number of people affected, life-shortening now appears to be the major deleterious effect of fallout.

We can summarize the situation this way. Our best estimate is that the chance of getting leukemia is one in 100,000 (it may be three times greater or less than this). The same applies to all other cancers together, and it turns out that the genetic risk also is about the same. The life-shortening effect cannot be expressed in terms of odds; all we can say is that many millions will be affected in some degree. Numerically we might say that it may amount to three million persons losing an average of three years of life, or 30 million losing four months, or three billion losing one day.

As I have pointed out, the uncertainties about these numbers are not important to the way I feel about fallout: the odds against damage are high enough so that I do not feel any special concern for the safety of my family or myself. Yet because the number of people seriously hurt is not zero, I feel I must ask whether the risks are justified. This takes us out of the area of science and into morals and politics in the broadest sense. Speaking now as a layman, I personally have two thoughts on this matter. The first is that there are many other areas of life in which we as a nation can and will affect more people's lives for better or worse, in pretty much the same broad statistical sense as by fallout. One medium-sized war anywhere in the world in the next 50 years, or the failure to prevent one major famine, would easily do more damage to life than fallout will.

The second thought is that fallout is not precisely the major issue with regard to the bomb tests. Behind this worry lies the much greater fear of nuclear war, and if we are truly concerned about war, then let us by all means use all our wisdom in going after that subject directly.

6 JAMES F. CROW

Radiation and Future Generations

Every human being starts out as a single cell, which came from the fusion of two cells—an egg from his mother and a sperm from his father. This cell divides into two, then into four, then into eight, and so on. By the time the child is born, there have been enough divisions to produce roughly ten million million cells. In growing from infancy to adulthood the number becomes some 20 times greater, and the process of replacement of defective or worn-out cells goes on continuously.

Every fertilized egg contains 46 thread-like or worm-like bodies, the chromosomes (see Plate I facing page 100). The 46 are of varying shapes and sizes but can be arranged in 23 matched pairs. One member of each pair came from the father via the sperm; the other came from the egg.

As the egg divides into two new cells, each of the 46 chromosomes divides longitudinally into two threads, one of which goes into each new cell. Thus each "daughter" cell has 46 chromosomes, one descended from each of the 46 in the initial cell. Because of this process, cells throughout the body have the same chromosomal make-up.

In the formation of the reproductive cells—the eggs and sperms—the process of chromosome distribution is slightly different. Each chromosome is duplicated, as usual, but there are two ensuing cell divisions instead of one, so that each sperm or egg cell gets only half as many chromosomes—23 instead of 46. Furthermore, these chromosomes always consist of one, and only one, representative of each of the 23 pairs carried by the person who produced the egg or sperm. When the egg is fertilized by the sperm, the double number, 46, is restored. Thus each child inherits exactly half of each parent's chromosomes. One quarter of his chromosomes, on the average, came from each grandparent, one eighth from each great-grandparent, and so on.

A typical cell in the human body is about $\frac{1}{2500}$ of an inch in diameter, a size which, although small, is easily visible with a microscope. The chromosomes also are visible, but in much less detail. It used to be thought that there were 48 chromosomes in the human cell, but with recently refined microscopic techniques we now see that the number is actually 46.

There is one exception to the statement that the two members of a chromosome pair are alike in appearance. In the pair known as the sex chromosomes the two members may differ. In a male cell one member of this pair is of about average size and one very small; they are called the X and Y chromosomes. A female cell, however, has two X chromosomes.

When a sperm cell forms in the male, it may carry either an X chromosome or a Y chromosome; every egg carries an X chromosome. If the egg is fertilized by a sperm carrying an X chromosome, the child has two X chromosomes and will develop into a female. If the sperm carries a Y chromosome, the fertilized egg is XY and develops into a male. Thus the sex of the child is determined at the time of conception by the chance that the successful sperm carries an X or Y chromosome. Notice that a boy always gets his X chromosome from his mother, and his Y from his father.

Along each chromosome, arranged in single file, are the genes—the units of heredity. The individual human gene is below the limits of visibility of the ordinary microscope, but the linear arrangement is inferred from experimental evidence and from observation of other organisms—notably the fruit fly, Drosophila. There is considerable evidence from recent work on Drosophila, fungi, viruses, and bacteria that the gene is divisible into finer units. In detailed genetic analysis the word gene may not be accurate enough, and other names have been introduced for precise genetic discourse. However, the distinctions are not necessary for this discussion and I shall use the good old-fashioned four-letter word "gene."

The genes are the determiners of hereditary traits. They exert their effect by influencing the body chemistry through chemical expediters known as enzymes, which regulate the multitude of chemical processes that go on in the organism. For example, one gene is known to be concerned with the enzyme that converts milk-sugar, galactose, into usable glucose. There is an aberrant form of this gene which fails to form the enzyme, and children born without the normal gene are unable to live on milk; they require substitutes not containing galactose.

As chromosomes occur in pairs, so must the genes. Usually if the two members of a gene pair are different, their influence is unequal. For example, a guinea pig with two genes for black hair color will have black hair. If he has two genes for white hair, he has white hair. What if he has one of each? Will he be gray? The answer is that he has black hair. Therefore we say that the black gene is dominant, because when both genes are present its trait dominates. Conversely the white gene is called recessive.

Most of the time dominance is not quite complete. For example, guinea pigs with one black and one white gene usually have occasional light hairs (which can serve as a marker showing that the genes are mixed). Another example is to be found in recessive lethal genes. If two such genes pair up, the animal cannot survive, but if it carries a normal counterpart along with the lethal gene, the effect may be just a statistical reduction in life expectancy.

Mutation

Ordinarily a gene copies itself unerringly through generation after generation. But occasionally it somehow mutates. For example, a gene that has been causing black pigment changes to one that produces brown pigment or no pigment at all. The mutation presumably is a chemical change in the gene. A mutant gene is just as stable as the original gene, so it can reproduce itself in its new form from generation to generation. Mutations occur in all parts of the body, but only those in reproductive tissues will be inherited. It is those that we are concerned with here.

Aside from gene mutations, there are sometimes gross alterations in chromosome structure, due to breakage of chromosomes and rearrangement of the broken parts. Such rearrangements can be detected by direct microscopic observation of the chromosomes. In addition there are minor rearrangements, too minute to be observed with a microscope, whose effects are indistinguishable from gene mutations. Thus mutation becomes a wastebasket category which includes both true mutations and small rearrangements in the chromosomes. (See Plates I–IV following page 100).

Mutation and chromosome breakage are exceedingly rare events. A typical mutation occurs about once in 100,000 generations. This means that a human gene goes through millions of years without mutating—an amazing instance of chemical stability and accuracy of duplication, for the gene must copy itself more than a million times during this period.

Despite the rarity of individual mutations, a mutation somewhere in the germ cell is not very rare, for there are thousands of genes at risk. If there are as many as 10,000 genes in a sperm cell, each of which has one chance in 100,000 of mutating, this means that one sperm in ten will carry a new mutation. These estimates are reasonable for Drosophila, and there is no reason to think that man is grossly different. So the total number of human mutations is substantial, despite the low probability for any individual gene.

Among the multitude of mutations that have occurred in the past of any species, man included, some were beneficial but most were harmful. Those that caused death or sterility or weakness of any sort tended to eliminate the hereditary lines that carried them. Consequently these mutant genes themselves, even if only slightly harmful, were eventually eliminated. On the other hand, mutant genes that brought some improvement in health or vigor tended to be preserved. Through this process, spread over long geological periods, evolution has occurred. Chance mutations arise, mostly harmful. The harmful ones disappear, while the small minority of beneficial mutants are retained. Thus natural selection converts the harmful process of mutation into evolutionary advance by erasing nature's mistakes. But the eliminations occur through disease, death, and impaired fertility.

What kinds of effects are produced by mutation? The simplest and probably most correct answer is: every kind. Geneticists studying human heredity have catalogued mutant genes that affect all parts of the body in all sorts of ways. The same is true for the mouse and other well-studied animals. In Drosophila there are mutants affecting the bristles, the eyes, the wings, and the legs. There are many more that are lethal—mutations that impair the embryonic development in some way so that the fly dies before reaching the adult stage. Others, probably the majority of all mutations, cause a statistical reduction in the life expectancy—not certain death but an enhanced probability of death.

Human data support this. There is reason to believe that genetic defects that owe their origin to mutation are uniquely revealed by inbreeding. Children of parents who are close relatives (e.g., cousins) have a slightly enhanced death rate. Furthermore, the effect is not usually due to diseases caused by known recessive genes. The majority of the deaths stem from other causes—childhood diseases, infections, even accidents. This must mean that the most common mutation is not a clearly recognizable genetic disease but an impairment of some body function, so that the individual is more likely to succumb to the various hardships and diseases of life.

This conclusion is strengthened by another consideration. Most mutant genes are recessive; that is, they produce their effect only in double dose. Many genetic diseases are of this sort. Yet, as mentioned earlier, there is abundant evidence from Drosophila and some direct evidence from mouse and human studies that most recessive factors have a slight effect even in a single dose. A single dose may cause something like 5 per cent as much harm as a double dose. Yet this 5 per cent is the most important part, for the reason that there are far more persons who have the gene in single dose than have it in double dose. A typical harmful recessive gene will usually be found hundreds of times more often in single dose than in double dose; so if the single-dose effect is only one per cent as much as the double, this is the part that causes the major impact on the population.

From the foregoing discussion we must conclude that only a small fraction of the mutations that occur produce conspicuous genetic diseases. The greater number exert their effects on the population in a milder and nonspecific way. But the fact that a mutant causes only a mild effect doesn't mean it is unimportant. A mutant gene that causes death is eliminated along with the person it kills, so only one individual is affected. But a mutant that produces a 50 per cent chance of death lives to strike another day: on the average it will affect two persons before being eliminated. And a gene causing one chance in 100 of death will affect a string of 100 persons before it is eliminated. If we adopt a system of mutation cost-accounting which postulates, say, that a 10 per cent risk to 100 persons is equivalent to a 100 per cent risk to 10 persons, then every mutant, whatever its intrinsic harmfulness, has to be considered to have an equal impact on the population. This principle was first pointed out by the English geneticist J. B. S. Haldane.

From the human standpoint this is a patent oversimplification, for a lingering, painful disease is a much greater tragedy than an early embryonic death. How do we compare the social burden of physical disease with that of mental disease? Or how do we put pain on a comparable scale with incapacitation? How do we regard diseases that are potentially curable? Furthermore, a gene may be extinguished from the population painlessly by the failure of its carrier to reproduce. It may, of course, be eliminated by chance, but this is exactly balanced by those that increase by chance.

The most innocuous mutant gene is one that is eliminated from the population painlessly and quickly. This may occur, for example, when a mutant causes an embryonic death which comes so early in the fertilized egg's development that it goes unnoticed. At the opposite end of the scale is a mutant gene which causes its bearers great pain or unhappiness but doesn't greatly influence their reproduction. Such a mutant may affect many persons before being eliminated. The social burden is especially great when a mutation causes mental disease and deficiency: the mutant gene then harms not only the afflicted individual but places a grave burden on his family and on society in general.

For all these reasons the problem of assessing the social burden of mutation is enormously complex and would be difficult to solve with precision even if we had detailed information on mutation rates and all the effects of mutant genes. One thing is clear: we must not discount the importance of mutant genes of small effect. They may be more important in the aggregate than grossly harmful ones.

Radiation and Mutation

In 1927 Hermann J. Muller announced his now famous discovery that fruit flies whose ancestors had been exposed to radiation showed an increased number of hereditary abnormalities. Subsequent studies in many kinds of plants and animals have abundantly confirmed his findings; in every organism studied, all kinds of high-energy radiation produce mutations if they reach the chromosomes.

Microscope studies have revealed that radiations are also effective as chromosome-breakers. They produce all sorts of chromosome aberrations. As with spontaneous mutations, it is impossible to distinguish between "true" mutations and minute chromosome losses or rearrangements.

The number of mutations produced has been shown to be directly proportional to the amount of radiation (except at high doses, which do not concern us here because we are dealing only with the low doses from fallout). Furthermore, the amount of effect is very nearly the same for different kinds of radiations; neutrons, X-rays, gamma rays, and the other radioactive by-products of nuclear energy are all of comparable effectiveness, provided they reach the chromosomes of the reproductive cells.

Geneticists are convinced that there is no threshold for radiation-induced mutations: that is, there is no dose so low that it produces no mutations at all. Each dose, however small, that reaches the germ cells between conception and reproduction carries a risk to future generations proportional to the dose.

The data supporting this conclusion come mainly from Drosophila studies. There is no significant departure from a proportional relation for dose ranges from several hundred roentgens down to 25 roentgens. Studies at lower doses have not been practicable. It is true that no experimental data exist for doses as low as those from fallout—at the present rate, something of the order of one tenth of a roentgen in our reproductive lifetime. However, there is no reason to think the proportion of damage changes at these doses. One argument for believing that the effect holds at low doses is the strict proportionality in the range of radiation that has been observed. Another is from purely physical considerations. At low doses there is an extremely small chance that two or more incident particles will overlap in their ionization paths, so there is no obvious physical basis for a nonproportional effect.

Until recently geneticists generally believed that the number of mutations produced by a given dose of radiation was the same irrespective of whether the radiation was given as one large dose or a succession of small ones, or whether the doses were given quickly or slowly. The basis for this conclusion was mostly from experiments on Drosophila, though there was supporting evidence from other organisms. But W. L. Russell at Oak Ridge has now reported that the rate of dosage does make a difference, at least for mouse germ cells in the stages before they develop into sperms or eggs. In his experiments, when the dose was spread out at low intensity it produced fewer mutants than the same dose given quickly at high intensity.

These studies make it necessary to re-evaluate earlier conclusions about the genetic effects of radiation on man. They raise the question whether the proportional concept is in fact correct. However, there is no indication of nonlinearity in the data at either dose rate. At the moment the best evidence is still that there is no "safe" dose, but that radiation given at a low rate is less effective than formerly was thought.

What have we learned from direct genetic studies on man? There are data from several sources. All the findings suggest a genetic effect, but none by itself is completely convincing. Stanley H. Macht and P. S. Lawrence, from a questionnaire survey, found the total incidence of stillbirths, miscarriages, and congenital abnormalities to be higher in the families of radiologists than in a control group of physicians who did not use radiation in their medical practice. However, in any questionnaire there is always the possibility that those who return the questionnaires are not typical of the entire group, and that the apparent radiation effect is spurious. Similar results are reported from a Japanese study of families of X-ray technicians, but once again, there are numerous possible sources of uncontrollable error.

A study was made in France of the children of parents who had been treated for spinal disease with heavy doses of radiation, much of which must have reached the reproductive cells.

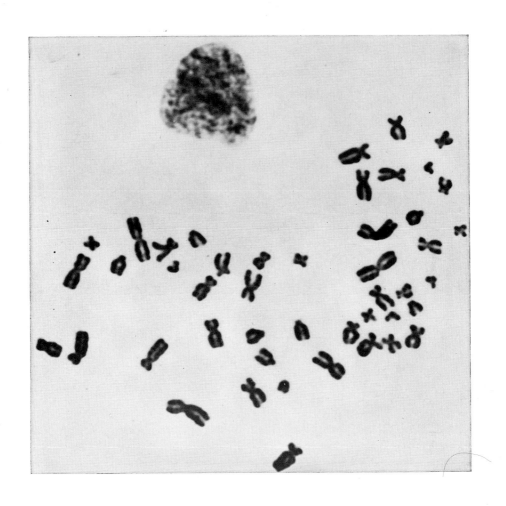

PLATE I. Photomicrograph of normal human chromosomes. [*From T. T. Puck, professor of biophysics, University of Colorado Medical Center.*]

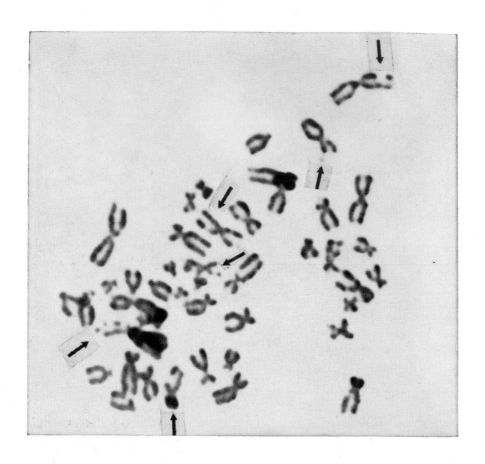

PLATE II. Chromosomes broken by irradiation with an X-ray dose of 75 roentgens. Arrows show the breaks. Such breaks soon reseal themselves. [*From T. T. Puck*, Proceedings of the National Academy of Sciences, *pp. 772–780, August, 1958.*]

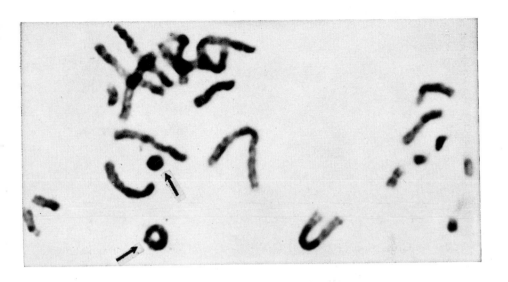

PLATES III (*above*) AND IV (*below*). Abnormal recombinations of broken chromosomes. These aberrant forms (see arrows) were formed after fracture of a number of chromosomes simultaneously by a dose of 150 roentgens. [*From T. T. Puck.*]

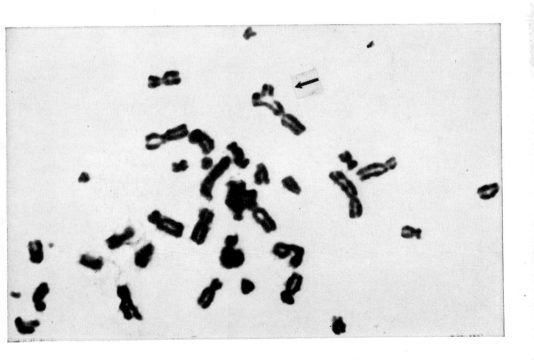

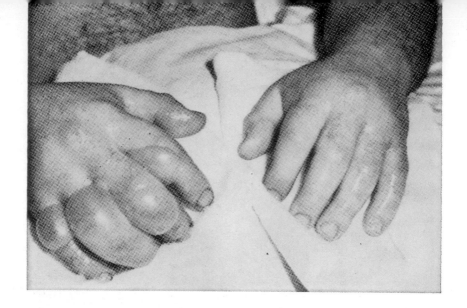

PLATE V. Gross damage to hands (three and one half days after radiation) resulting from exposure to intense flux of neutrons and gamma rays in the first lethal accident at Los Alamos Scientific Laboratory. [*From L. H. Hempelman, H. Lisco, and J. G. Hoffman, "The Acute Radiation Syndrome,"* Annals of Internal Medicine, *February 1952.*]

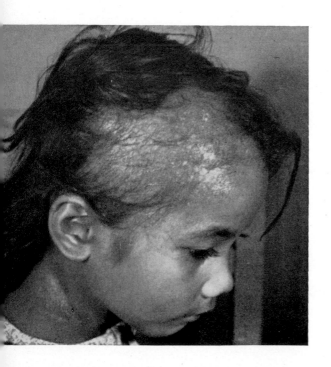

PLATE VI. Marshall Island child injured by fallout from the March 1, 1954, hydrogen-bomb test in the Pacific. The photograph shows the skin burns and loss of hair 28 days after the exposure. Six months later the skin lesions had healed and the hair had grown back. [*From E. P. Cronkite, V. P. Bond, and C. L. Dunham, "Some Effects of Ionizing Radiation on Human Beings," published by United States Atomic Energy Commission, July, 1956.*]

The investigators found, again by questionnaire, that there were fewer sons in families where the mother had been irradiated than in those in which the father was the one irradiated. Recall that the male receives his X chromosome from his mother. Hence any deleterious recessive genes induced by the radiation would injure the sons of an irradiated mother but not the daughters (see Figure 16). The study of Hiroshima and Nagasaki survivors has shown the same shift in sex ratio.

So, all told, there is considerable direct evidence of a genetic effect in man. But of much more importance is the overwhelming evidence in all experimental organisms that have been tested. After all, we too are members of the animal kingdom.

Quantitative Estimates

From the evidence presented so far it seems beyond doubt that radiations produce mutations in man. When it comes to quantitative estimates, we are on shaky ground, because the human data are inadequate for more than the crudest of quantitative statements and the results in experimental animals differ from one species to another.

For example, mice seem to be about 18 times as mutable as fruit flies for a given amount of radiation. This raises the frightening possibility that man may be much more susceptible to radiation-induced mutation than the mouse. The mouse is larger and has a longer life cycle than the fruit fly and is more susceptible; does that mean that man is proportionately more mutable than the mouse? We are in no position to answer this definitely, but the data from Hiroshima and Nagasaki offer some argument against this possibility. If man were 20 times as mutable as the mouse, this should have been detectable in the studies of the children of bomb survivors. So it is not likely that man is *grossly* more susceptible than the mouse, but he could be somewhat more.

In the absence of better information, about all that can be

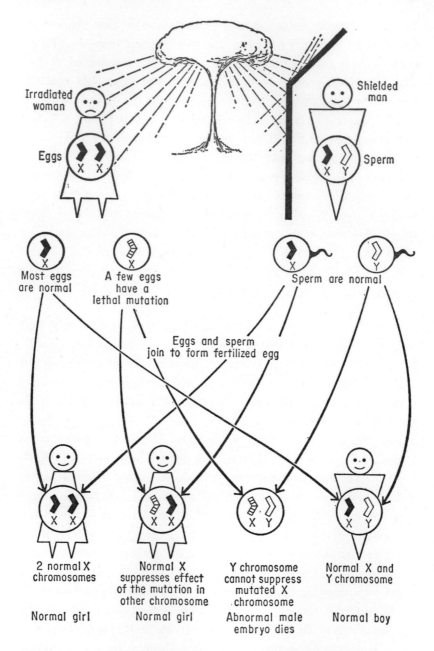

FIG. 16. How radiation affects the boy-girl ratio of births when one parent (the mother) is irradiated.

done is to use data on mice—the closest animal to man on which we have quantitative information. It should be clearly understood that all estimates of future genetic damage, here or elsewhere, have depended on mouse data. The estimates may therefore be very far off.

The United Nations Report on the Effects of Atomic Radiation estimated that 4 per cent of all human infants now have or will develop serious hereditary defects. It is not known what fraction of these are directly attributable to the mutation rate. The reason is that some of the harmful genes in the population are not maintained by recurrent mutation but by other mechanisms. For example, some genes are beneficial in a single dose but harmful in a double dose. Increasing the mutation rate of such genes would cause less effect on the population than a corresponding increase in a mutant that is unequivocally harmful. Unfortunately we don't know which kind of gene is most responsible for the 4 per cent rate of genetic defects among infants.

The United Nations committee estimated that a permanent doubling of the mutation rate would cause the 4 per cent to rise eventually to 5 to 8 per cent. The time required for this to reach its final value would be dozens of generations.

From Russell's mouse studies, using his results with a slow dose rate as comparable to fallout radiation, we find that each roentgen produces about five mutations per 100 million genes exposed. The spontaneous mutation rate in man is about one per 100,000 genes. On this basis a population exposed to one roentgen would have its mutation rate increased by a factor of 0.005 (5/100,000,000 divided by 1/100,000). If, as the UN committee estimates, a doubling of the mutation rate would increase genetic diseases by something like 1 to 4 per cent—let us say 2.5 per cent—we can calculate the effect of a 0.005 rise in mutation rate as .005 x .025, or roughly 1/8000. Thus, after a number of generations of exposure to one roentgen per generation, about one in 8,000 of the population in each generation would have severe genetic defects attributable to the radiation. In other words, the increase would be about a hundredth of one per cent —that is, from 4 to 4.01 per cent.

These figures are, of course, highly uncertain and may be off by a factor of ten in either direction. However, they are much more likely to underestimate than overestimate the total impact, because they consider only those genes that cause serious genetic diseases.

As mentioned earlier, most mutant genes have comparatively mild effects. Yet because these affect so many more persons they may be just as important or more important than drastic mutations. To consider only the drastic effects because they are more certain seems to me to be like ignoring the part of the iceberg that is under water. Once again we can use mouse data to estimate the total effect. Assuming that the total mutation rate for all genes is 20,000 times that for any single gene (this number has been determined with reasonable accuracy only in Drosophila), we find that one roentgen would produce one mutation per 1,000 animals. (Remember that these hypothetical animals have the mutation rate of a mouse and the gene number of a Drosophila.) In a population of one million there would be 1,000 mutations.

If we recall that each mutant must remain in the population until it is eliminated by the premature death or failure to reproduce of some individual, there would be 1,000 eliminations, or what Muller calls "genetic deaths." As emphasized earlier, some mutants are eliminated early and painlessly; others are finally eliminated only after causing pain or disease or unhappiness to a whole series of people. There is no way to assess the impact of these mutations, but we can estimate their number.

If our hypothetical population of one million organisms had been exposed to one roentgen, there would be about 1,000 mutations or one per 1,000 individuals. If the population had been exposed to one roentgen per generation for many generations, there would be 1,000 new mutations each generation and

1,000 eliminations of old mutations through failure to survive or reproduce.

According to the UN committee, the radiation from the fall-out of the bomb tests up to 1958 is about 0.01 roentgen. If the present world population has a total of two billion children, these would inherit an estimated 20,000 mutations as a result of the fallout. If tests continued at the 1954–1958 rate for a 30-year generation, the number would rise about tenfold—to 200,000. This is about 1/2000 of the mutations expected from other causes, or one thirtieth of the number that would be produced in the same period by natural radiations.

We live in a constantly changing environment. What was a severe mutant last generation may be mild today. Yet it still seems true that the effect of an environmental advance is usually to ameliorate rather than obliterate the genetic defect; hence the effect is to postpone rather than eliminate the damage to the population. I have discussed this, as well as other problems of estimating mutational effects in man, in more detail elsewhere (*Eugenics Quarterly*, 3:201–208; 4:67–80).

I should like to emphasize the crudity of these calculations and the tenuousness of the assumptions, especially the necessity of relying entirely on experimental animals. The calculations may be seriously wrong, and give only a very rough idea of the probable magnitudes involved. Equally plausible assumptions could give values several times higher or lower. Nevertheless, the following general conclusion seems clear: The amount of genetic damage due to fallout and other man-made radiation is small relative to mutation from other causes. Yet, considering the size of the present and future world population, this small fraction can be a very large number.

7 GOULD A. ANDREWS

Radiation Accidents

As Walter Guild pointed out in Chapter 5, much of our information about the effects of radiation on man has come from intensive studies of victims of accidents. There have been only a few such incidents, but they are so dramatic and terrifying that they have served as subjects for novels as well as for scientific study. This chapter will briefly review the principal serious accidents.

What is most remarkable is the fact that so few accidents have occurred in the many projects of the Atomic Energy Commission. Atomic energy installations have proved to be among the safest of all factories in which to work. This fine safety record is due to careful planning based upon recognition of the hazards of radiation. Most of the mishaps that have occurred in the atomic energy program have been ordinary injuries not involving radiation at all. However, the rare radiation accidents have had a great deal of publicity, which is not surprising in view of the natural tendency to fear the unknown, the insidious nature of the radiation hazard, and the vivid memory of the effects of the atom bombs in Japan.

The most serious accidents have involved in each case a single heavy dose of external radiation to the whole body. There is some uncertainty as to just what the lethal dose is for a human being. In animal studies, the different species have shown considerable variation in tolerance. For man, the best estimate is that the "lethal dose 50 per cent" (LD-50), the amount that will kill half of those exposed within a short time, is between 300 and 600 rads. At these doses the symptoms follow a characteristic course. In the first day or two, the patient suffers severe nausea and vomiting, and there is a drop in his count of lymphocytes (one type of white blood cell). After the nausea and vomiting subside, the patient may feel quite well for three weeks or so. In the third week he may begin to lose his hair. Soon afterward comes a sharp drop in the white cells and platelets (the clotting elements that prevent bleeding), because the damaged bone marrow's ability to produce them gives out. The patient develops infections or bleeding or both. This is the critical stage with the LD-50 dose. But if the marrow damage is not too severe, it is often possible to save the patient's life with antibiotics for the infections and transfusions of blood or platelets. Even more effective than blood, it now appears, may be injections of bone-marrow cells from a donor.

At doses much higher than the LD-50, there are other symptoms and the victim dies within days; so far no helpful treatment for such doses has been found.

The Early Los Alamos Accidents

During the year 1945–1946, two serious nuclear accidents occurred at the Los Alamos Scientific Laboratory in New Mexico. Both were caused by the inadvertent and momentary creation of supercritical assemblies of fissionable material during experiments in the laboratory. Ten persons altogether were exposed to the bursts of neutrons and gamma rays from these uncontrolled chain reactions, but only two got fatal doses. One received about 2,000 roentgens and died in nine days. The other had about 600 roentgens and died a "marrow death" in 26 days. A striking aspect of these exposures was severe, visible damage to the tissues of the hands, arms, and front of the body (*e.g.*, bulbous swellings of the fingers—see Plate V).

The eight other persons exposed to the two accidents recovered, but one developed cataracts in both eyes after three years. All the patients were studied exhaustively by L. H. Hempelmann and a large group of associates. Their report, published in *The Annals of Internal Medicine* of February, 1952, is a classic study on radiation effects in man.

The 1954 Fallout Incident

Earlier chapters in this book have already described the accident in the bomb test of March, 1954, when, because of an unexpected change in the wind, concentrations of fallout dropped on the Marshall Islanders, on ships taking part in the bomb test, and on the *Lucky Dragon*. The Atomic Energy Commission, in cooperation with the United States Navy, made a careful clinical and laboratory study of the Marshall Islanders, and E. P. Cronkite and a large group of collaborators presented the results in a document entitled *Some Effects of Ionizing Radiation on Human Beings*, published by the Atomic Energy Commission in July, 1953.

The patients received gamma-ray doses of up to 175 roentgens to the whole body and also ingested some radioactively contaminated food. All, however, survived the experience without apparent permanent injury (see Plate VI). Some of them had pigmented areas at the sites of skin ulcerations.

The *Lucky Dragon* fishermen showed effects of whole-body irradiation and skin changes from radioactive particles deposited on their bodies. Between 30 and 45 days after the exposure they suffered weakness, hemorrhage, and infection. One man died, more than six months after the exposure, of a liver disorder which apparently was due not directly to radiation damage but to an infection transmitted to him through the blood transfusions he had received as treatment.

The Windscale Accident

On October 10, 1957, a British reactor known as the "Windscale No. 1 Pile" sprang some leaks as a result of accidental overheating. Filters in the stack prevented most of the released fission product particles from escaping, but some material was sprayed over the countryside—chiefly radioactive iodine. The main concern was the possibility that cows eating the grass would pass on the radioiodine in their milk. It had been suggested that the safe limit of iodine 131 in milk was about 0.4 of a microcurie per liter. Two days after the accident some milk samples from the area near the reactor were found to contain twice this amount—0.8 of a microcurie per liter. The authorities ordered milk deliveries stopped temporarily in a two-mile radius around the Windscale reactor. Further analyses showed that a still wider area was unsuitable for milk production, and the restrictions on distribution were extended. This temporary measure adequately controlled the hazard from radioiodine. The largest amount of iodine found in the thyroid gland of any person living in the neighborhood was 0.28 of a microcurie measured in a child. This was not considered serious, because a *continuous* level of 0.1 of a microcurie in the thyroid was regarded as safe. Fortunately no one suffered any appreciable injury from the Windscale accident, although there was a good deal of public alarm.

The nearest approach to a serious radiation effect probably occurred in children who drank significant amounts of milk produced in the area before the extent of the hazard was realized. The accident showed that control of milk is one of the first safety precautions that must be taken when there is any possibility of airborne dissemination of fission products. It also taught some lessons about reactor management. Newer power reactors make less use of graphite, in which the fire developed at Windscale, so this particular problem is less likely to arise in the future.

The Oak Ridge Incident

On June 16, 1958, there was a uranium chain-reaction accident in the Oak Ridge chemical factory known as Y-12 (originally built to separate uranium 235 by the electromagnetic method). A large amount of enriched uranium 235 was inadvertently allowed to flow into a drum intended to hold only water. The operator nearest the drum noticed yellow-brown fumes (from chemicals associated with uranium) arising from the drum. Within a few seconds there was a bluish flash. Five men were near the drum; they fled as the evacuation siren sounded. It was soon determined that a criticality accident had occurred. The doses the men had received could be measured with considerable precision. By repeating the essential features of the accident in a mock-up experiment, by measuring the radioactive sodium in the victims' blood as an indication of their exposure to neutrons, and by estimating the gamma-ray doses with other techniques, it was determined that the five men had had between 236 and 365 rads. Three other men in the room had between 25 and 100 rads.

The five men with the highest doses developed nausea within two hours after the accident. They showed the characteristic blood changes of severe radiation injury. After the nausea and vomiting, which persisted for two or three days, the men felt quite well. On the seventeenth day they began to notice loss of hair. Between the twenty-fifth and thirtieth days they showed a mild tendency to bleed, associated with a pronounced decrease in platelets in the blood. There were also some incidental infections, but these were easily controlled with drugs. During the fourth and fifth weeks after exposure, production of cells by their bone marrow dropped sharply; however, it quickly recovered spontaneously. The men suffered some muscular weakness for several months after the accident but eventually regained normal health.

The Yugoslav Incident

A very serious radiation accident occurred on October 15, 1958, in the Yugoslavian atomic energy installation near Belgrade; and studies of the accident were published by Drs. G. Mathé, H. Jammet, and others in the *Revue Française D'Études Cliniques et Biologiques* of April, 1959. A criticality reaction developed accidentally in this heavy-water reactor and persisted for many minutes. Six workers in the neighborhood of the reactor were not aware of the danger. Instruments designed to give warning of high radiation levels were not in operation at the time. Eventually the accident was recognized, and it was realized that the six persons had received very high doses of gamma and neutron radiation. Accurate estimation of the doses was not possible, however, partly because the men walked around in the room at various distances from the reactor during the period of criticality. (A re-enactment of the accident has since been arranged, and with the use of dummies it is hoped to get better estimates of the doses they received.)

The victims quickly developed nausea, vomiting, and weakness. The day after the accident they were flown to the Curie Foundation in Paris for treatment. (Their arrival started a false rumor that they were dangerously radioactive and had contaminated the Paris airport.)

The patient with the highest radiation dose became acutely ill about three weeks after the exposure, with a complex disease picture. He had evidence of some abdominal disorder, as well as failure of the kidneys and the usual severe bone-marrow depression. He was given an injection of blood-forming cells from a human embryo, but this did not help. Later he received marrow cells from an adult donor. There was some evidence that the transfused cells began to grow successfully, but in spite of this the patient died a month after the accident.

The marrow-transplantation experiment apparently was more

effective, however, in the four patients with the next highest doses. As the level of the depressed blood elements rose toward normal, special studies showed that red cells of the donor type were being produced. After a few weeks the patients' own marrow again became the chief source of red cells; the grafted marrow then apparently declined. This was presumably fortunate, because the foreign tissue would tend to produce an undesirable immune reaction (see Chapter 8).

The four patients who received the bone marrow made a good recovery from their radiation injury. The sixth patient, who did not require any bone-marrow treatment, also made a satisfactory recovery.

There is some disagreement about the effects of the bone-marrow graft in the Yugoslavian victims. Because the size of their radiation doses was not well established, it has been argued that they might have survived even without the marrow treatment. This writer believes that the clinical and laboratory picture was compatible with a high radiation dosage and that the evidence is strong that the marrow was beneficial. Thus it appears that this technique is an important step forward in the treatment of radiation injury.

The Largest Dose

A criticality accident occurred at Los Alamos on December 30, 1958. It took place during the recovery of plutonium produced in a reactor. Normally this fissionable product is handled only in small quantities, so that there is no danger of its reaching critical dimensions. But through an error three batches (in different stages of purification) were put in a large tank together. When an electric stirring device was turned on, it worked the plutonium into a critical configuration. There was a sudden blue flash and a "muffled report." The workman who had turned on the electric stirrer and was looking into the tank was thrown from a low ladder on which he was standing. He immediately ran outside the building and cried that he was burning up. His skin quickly reddened. Within a few minutes he began to vomit and to discharge a profuse, watery diarrhea. He was taken to the hospital in shock. Vigorous treatment with intravenous fluids failed to maintain a normal blood pressure. He died 36 hours after the exposure. Blood studies showed a pronounced rise in his total white-cell count but a complete absence of lymphocytes a few hours after the accident. Autopsy studies indicated considerable damage to the heart muscle. His chest had been closest to the part of the tank where the fission occurred and had received the highest dose.

This patient probably represents the highest dose of whole-body irradiation that has ever been studied in man. His death had some of the features of gastrointestinal death and some of the features of "central nervous system" death. The damage to the heart had not been seen in any other radiation victim.

Another employee, who had been about 40 feet away from the nuclear burst, received a significant radiation exposure when he entered the area to help the first operator. His dose, however, was not high enough to produce any clinical evidence of radiation illness.

This accident, like the Y-12 accident at Oak Ridge, occurred in an area where fissionable material was processed and where it was presumed that there was little danger of a criticality accident. Subsequent detective work led to a clear understanding of the events that had led to the excessive concentration of fissionable material. There are clear-cut ways of preventing a recurrence of such an accident.

All of the nuclear accidents described in this chapter are easily explained on known physical principles. Each involved some failure to take sufficient precautions or to consider the possibility of an unusual set of coincidences. Improved precautionary measures were put into effect afterward, and some of the types of accidents described are unlikely to happen again. However, with the greatly increased number of reactors that will be in operation in future years, and the widespread use of radioisotopes, there will undoubtedly be more accidents of one type or another. Under the best of circumstances the world will have need of much more knowledge about how to treat victims of radiation, and physicians and nurses must be trained in this field.

With adequate precautions, mankind need not fear radiation. Let us bear in mind that, in comparison with other new technological developments, nuclear science, at least in its peaceable aspects, has been remarkably safe.

8 JACK SCHUBERT

Protection and
Treatment

Radiation injures or kills in so many ways that we cannot expect
to find any single treatment that will give blanket protection.
For instance, although bone-marrow injections may cope effectively with one of the most serious forms of acute injury, they
will not protect against long-range effects such as cancer or
life-shortening. For another example, there are drugs that protect an animal if given before its exposure to radiation but do
not help if given afterward. Moreover, none of the treatments
so far conceived would be practicable for large populations.
Nonetheless, it is encouraging that despite the complexities of
radiation's harmful effects, some promising methods of combating them have been uncovered.

The search for treatments goes on unabated in laboratories
around the world. Since we do not know exactly how radiation
damages living matter, most of the investigations must proceed
empirically—that is, by trial and error. It is hoped that bigger
and better trial-and-error experiments (dignified by the name
"screening programs") will hit upon new and more effective
treatments. The search for protections against radiation is much
like the present search for treatments or cures for cancer. Indeed, the connection is very close, because in both cases our
ideas about the fundamental biological mechanisms involved

are largely conjectural and in both cases attention is centered on the chemistry of the living cell.

It is generally accepted that the effects of radiation stem from breakdown of atoms and molecules in the cell into ions. For example, radiation splits the water molecule into the very active "free radicals" H (a free atom of hydrogen) and OH (hydroxyl). These go on to produce damage by reacting with sensitive parts of the cell. Radiation can also injure the cell more directly by attacking a so-called "sensitive volume" in the cell.

The search for treatments has focused mainly on two objectives: (1) to prevent or counteract the effect itself, and (2) to remove the source of radiation when it is lodged inside the body (*e.g.*, ingested fallout particles). Two classes of treatment substances have been explored: "protective agents," which are given shortly *before* or *during* the irradiation; and "recovery agents," given *after* the irradiation.

Protective Agents

The protective agents may act in one of several ways. They may react with the free radicals and thus neutralize them, they may shield the sensitive parts of the cells from the free radicals or other poisonous substances, or they may protect by reducing the concentration of oxygen, which under certain conditions reacts with the hydrogen and hydroxyl free radicals to form damaging oxidizers (*e.g.*, hydrogen peroxide).

Among the protective agents that have proved most effective in animal experiments are those which possess a sulfhydryl group (SH), consisting of a sulfur atom combined with a hydrogen atom. That such compounds could protect animals given normally lethal doses of radiation was first reported in 1949 by Harvey M. Patt and his associates at the Argonne National Laboratory. They found that injections or oral doses of the amino acid cysteine could reduce the number of deaths. Two related compounds, cysteamine and cystamine, also proved to be effective.

By systematic modification of the structure of molecules such as cysteine and cysteamine, David G. Doherty and his collaborators at Oak Ridge discovered a compound which showed more promise than any previously tested. This new substance, called AET, breaks down in the body to one named MEG, which functions as the protective agent.

It is reasonable to expect that these drugs will have about the same action in human beings as they have had in laboratory experimental animals; AET has proved its ability to protect monkeys. All of the agents reduce various damaging effects of X-rays—hair loss, blood-cell depletion, and the death rate. This suggests that they act at an early stage in the general chain of events that leads to radiation damage—probably during the formation of free radicals. They are less effective against damage produced by heavily ionizing particles such as alpha particles and neutrons, probably because the latter can give rise to poisonous oxidizing substances even in the absence of oxygen. And of course high doses of any radiation can overwhelm their protective effect. For example, although a protective agent may enable most of a group of experimental animals to survive the normally lethal dose (LD-50) of 650 rads, it is of little avail against a dose of 1,300 rads.

Under certain conditions physical factors such as cold, shielding of parts of the body, and dehydration of tissues (*e.g.*, by drinking alcohol) give some protection against radiation damage. It would appear that in case of a surprise nuclear attack the individuals most likely to survive the radiation would be those caught dead drunk in an underground cold-storage room.

Recovery Agents

The object of treatment given after irradiation is twofold: to deal with the immediate damage and to prevent development

of delayed effects. We are in no position yet to say what, if anything, can be done to prevent the long-range effects, but a great
step forward has at least been taken with the discovery of
methods that can save lives by helping the body's processes of
spontaneous recovery from acute damage.

In the accidents described in the preceding chapter, the
victims of very large doses of radiation were given certain "sup-
portive" treatments designed to make them more comfortable
and if possible to prevent death. These treatments are: anti-
hemorrhagic drugs to control bleeding, blood transfusions,
liquids to maintain the fluid and mineral balance, and antibiotics to control infection. After Leon O. Jacobson and his
co-workers at Argonne found in 1949 that shielding the spleen,
a blood-forming organ, could protect animals against lethal
doses of radiation, spleen extracts were tried as an additional
treatment. Then the late Egon Lorenz and his associates at
the National Cancer Institute discovered the value of injection
of bone-marrow cells, and this therapy was first used in the fall
of 1958. It was the first specific recovery agent to show successful results in man.

Transplants of bone-marrow cells provide blood-forming cells
which enable the patient to survive until his own blood-forming cells regenerate. The main problem is that any graft of
foreign cells causes the body to produce antibodies which destroy the injected cells. It turns out, however, in a sense fortunately, that radiation impairs the body's ability to produce
antibodies, and so the foreign cells are able to survive for a
time. But if the patient is to recover, his own cells must eventually destroy the injected cells after they have served their
temporary purpose. In the first trial of the bone-marrow treatment, the patients' own recovering cells seemingly won out over
the transplants.

This initial use of the treatment was applied to the victims of
the 1958 Yugoslavian reactor accident described in the preceding chapter. Of the six persons exposed, one was estimated to
have received a dose of roughly 1,000 rem, four others doses

ranging from 400 to 600 rem, and the sixth a dose of perhaps 200 rem. Their symptoms indicated that at least three of the six would die within a few months.

At the Curie Hospital of the Pasteur Foundation in Paris, where they were taken, the group of physicians and research specialists handling their care—Drs. Jammet, Mathé, Duplan, Maupin, and Pendic—decided to try the bone-marrow treatment. They gave the patients no blood transfusions, lest these produce antibodies, nor antibiotics, lest the drugs interfere with the growth of bone-marrow cells. The first transplant tried was an injection of blood-forming liver cells from a five-month human fetus; fetal cells were chosen because they make less antibody than adult cells do and therefore would not strongly inhibit the cells of the patient. But this treatment produced no response in the patient. The five most seriously injured patients were then given injections of bone marrow from healthy donors with the same blood types (to minimize antibody formation). The marrow was drawn from the donor's bone with a syringe and then immediately injected into the arm of the patient. Each patient received roughly half a pint of bone marrow, corresponding to about 10 to 15 billion cells.

The response to the transplantation was immediate. The patients' white blood-cell count increased rapidly, and their blood became approximately normal within a week. The patient with the heaviest radiation dose (about 1,000 rem) died of intestinal damage, which could not be repaired, but all the others recovered. Two months later the proportion of donor cells among their red blood cells had dropped to one third, which showed that the patients were now regenerating their own cells. And they exhibited no serious antibody reactions. Research workers will keep track of these Yugoslavian patients for the rest of their lives to see whether delayed effects of the irradiation appear.

Although spleen or bone-marrow cells seem effective against acute damage to the bone from gamma rays, this treatment is not likely to prevent death from neutrons, which cause heavy damage to the stomach and intestines.

Some experiments have been made in combining protective and recovery treatments in irradiated animals. It has been found that if rats receive AET before irradiation and the bone-marrow treatment afterward, they withstand higher doses of radiation than would have been possible with either treatment alone.

Clearly this whole field of research is still in its infancy. There is not even a suggestion of any treatment that could be used on a large scale or would protect against continual small radiation doses from the general environment. But a heavily supported program of research into new methods of treatment is under way, and many scientists are studying the ways in which radiation injures cells, in the hope that such knowledge will furnish clues to a simple and specific treatment against both the short- and the long-term effects of radiation.

Removal of Internal Radioisotopes

Getting rid of radioactive material that enters the body is a complex and difficult problem, because of the chemical differences among the fallout elements and the variety of their destinations. These radioisotopes can get into the body by several routes: via food and drink, via the air we breathe, or through breaks in the skin (*e.g.*, when the skin is cut by a contaminated instrument). Although much of the radioactive material is eliminated naturally in the urine and feces, the part that is incorporated in the tissues of the body tends to stay there a long time. Strontium 90 is the outstanding example: it seems practically impossible to remove it once it becomes fixed in the bones.

The aim of treatment, therefore, must be to trap and remove the radioactive substances promptly while they are still in the bloodstream or some other accessible place—that is, before they have become deposited in inaccessible tissues.

For some radioisotopes, such as plutonium 239 and the rare earths, the best treatment is no treatment, when they are taken in by mouth. Very little of these substances can be absorbed from the digestive tract into the bloodstream, because they are insoluble. Consequently they are largely eliminated in the feces. But strontium 90, which behaves chemically like calcium, *is* soluble, and from 25 to 50 per cent of the amount swallowed tends to be absorbed into the bloodstream and rapidly deposited in the tissues. Much research has been done on the possibility of rendering ingested strontium insoluble so that it will be eliminated instead of traveling to the bone.

The methods under study are still in the experimental stage and do not look promising for general use. Even under the best conditions it appears that the treatment must be given within minutes after strontium has been swallowed. And there are important obstacles to applying the treatments in question to large human populations. To minimize the absorption of strontium taken in daily in food would require daily doses of chemicals added to the diet. These chemicals might not be tolerated well by all segments of the world population. Even the apparently simple procedure of adding calcium salts to the diet (to dilute the strontium) might well cause such disturbances of the physiological balance in large numbers of people as to outweigh the advantage gained by a slight reduction in the absorption of strontium 90.

Some measures might be helpful in specific situations. Where people have a diet low in calcium, enrichment of their foods with strontium-free calcium salts might appreciably reduce the amount of strontium retained by the body. One simple and practical protection is to keep infants on mother's milk for several months. It has been found that mother's milk contains far less strontium 90 than cow's milk—a fine argument for breast feeding!

It may be possible to reduce the amount of strontium 90 in our milk and meat by adding calcium to cattle feeds. There are also ways to remove strontium 90 directly from milk. For example, about 90 per cent or more of strontium 90 can be removed by means of synthetic plastics called ion exchangers.

These materials have an affinity for strontium ions and leave most of the other components of milk undisturbed. Although ion-exchange treatment would be useful in special cases of very high contamination, it does not appear necessary or suitable for use at the present time.

For radioactive material deposited on the skin, the best treatment is to wash or shower as soon as possible with a copious flow of water; chemicals capable of dissolving the radioelements also may be needed to get rid of local concentrations. When insoluble radioactive material gets into a cut in the skin, it may be necessary to cut away the contaminated flesh and then flush the wound with water.

What can be done if the radioisotope reaches the bloodstream? The most effective treatment known so far is the use of substances called "chelating agents." Named from the Greek word *chela*, meaning the claws of a lobster or crab, these substances grab metal ions and hold them tightly in a kind of chemical cage. The combination usually is so soluble that it tends to be removed easily from the tissues and pass into the urine. One of the most widely known chelating agents is a synthetic substance called EDTA (for ethylenediaminetetra-acetic acid). Figure 17 is a simplified picture showing how EDTA seizes strontium from its sodium salt.

There is another chelating agent, called DTPA, which has more "claws" for holding on to metals and appears to be superior to EDTA.

Plutonium and the rare earths are most susceptible to the action of EDTA and DTPA. A single injection of DTPA can increase the excretion of plutonium as much as 50 times or more, and it works even when the plutonium has been in the body for several days. However, if the plutonium is in the tissues, the treatment has to be given intermittently for a long period to remove significant amounts of it.

Since DTPA and EDTA must be injected into the bloodstream for best results, it would be impracticable to apply this treatment to a population poisoned by plutonium and rare

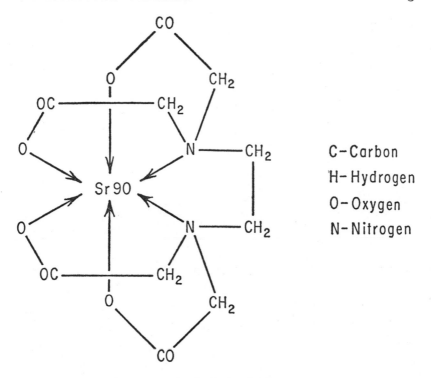

FIG. 17. Capture of strontium 90 by the EDTA molecule.

earths on a large scale. What is desired is a simple, nonpoisonous substance which would be effective when taken by mouth.

For strontium 90, EDTA and DTPA are simply out of the question as a treatment. They hold calcium more tightly than they do its chemical brother strontium, so they tend to remove calcium rather than the harmful radioisotope. There are chelating agents that can pick up strontium, but they remove appreciable amounts from the body only while a large proportion of the ingested strontium is circulating in the bloodstream. The possibility of finding an agent that will eliminate strontium 90 after it has become locked in bone must be considered remote.

Summing up the results of the search for treatments of radiation damage, we are compelled to conclude that the situation is best expressed by the old proverb: "An ounce of prevention is worth a pound of cure!"

9 CHET HOLIFIELD

Civil Defense

The enormously destructive effects of modern weapons, discussed in detail elsewhere in this volume, have led large segments of the American public to believe that nothing could be done to save lives in the event of a large-scale nuclear attack. Many Americans simply have refused to consider any civil-defense effort as feasible in the face of such a national calamity.

The problem of civil defense, however, is not one of saving everybody in the event of attack. Obviously persons caught in the direct path of a nuclear weapon would not survive. But the vast majority of the casualties in a nuclear attack would be suffered among persons *not* directly hit by the bombs. These casualties might be avoided if the population were provided with moderate shielding against fallout, emergency food and medical supplies, instructions on how to avoid unnecessary exposure in contaminated areas, and other civil-defense measures which are within the realm of feasibility.

The task of civil defense is to determine what can be done to *minimize* the effects of a possible enemy attack and then to prepare a program to accomplish this objective.

Its accomplishment has been hampered by indecision. Whose is the chief responsibility for the program? What shall be the basic approach to the solution—shelters or evacuation? These are the questions needing answers. Let us examine them.

Federal or State Responsibility?

The Civil-Defense Act of 1950 placed operational responsibility at the state level. Each state was expected to plan, organize, and operate its own program, with the Federal Civil Defense Administration serving as a source of technical information and policy guidance. The Act specifically stated that "responsibility for civil defense shall be vested primarily in the several states and their political subdivisions." This virtual abdication of power by the Federal Government set the tone and theme of civil defense at the Federal level that has prevailed until the present time. Civil defense in this country has not yet fully recovered from that initial limitation attached to Federal participation.

With the limitations at the Federal level, civil defense has been little more than a public education program. The people have been urged to build basement and backyard shelters and to store food stocks for emergency use. Training courses and study guides have been presented on first-aid, fire-fighting, and rescue services. Federal funds furnished to the states for civil-defense purposes have been used to purchase fire trucks, emergency water piping, and various items of equipment suitable for combating relatively minor disasters. Additional Federal funds, amounting to nearly $10 million, have been poured into studies of the feasibility of evacuation, under the Survival Planning Projects initiated in 1956 by the Federal Civil Defense Administration.

All of these efforts, useful as they may seem individually, on the whole represent a crude and primitive approach to the highly complicated task of protecting the nation from thermonuclear weapons.

A principal cause of the disjointed and disparate efforts in civil defense to date has been the failure of the Federal Government to set forth realistic objectives and establish a long-range program to achieve those objectives. One of the most notable failures in this respect has been the Federal approach to shelters.

Run or Dig?

When the 1950 legislation was under consideration, deep community shelters were contemplated, and a Federal contribution of $1,125,000,000 was proposed. Soon after passage of the law, however, the emphasis was changed from deep shelters to above-ground shelters, improvised by reinforcing existing structures. Requests for shelter-construction funds were presented to the Congress for several years, but no money was appropriated.

In 1951 a plea for improvised above-ground shelters was made by the first FCDA Administrator, Millard Caldwell, for the following stated reasons:

> In the first place, we will probably not be able to give adequate warning to all the people who could get in [deep] shelters. In the second place, it will take too long to construct them. In the third place, they will use too much in the way of labor and critical materials, steel, and concrete. Therefore, new emphasis must be put on making the most out of whatever we have wherever we find it, identifying those places which can be made fairly safe by shoring up. They are available now. We cannot wait for the deep-shelter program.

Administrator Caldwell estimated that "we can locate or prepare simple, inexpensive shelter for 30 million Americans who will need it if an attack comes." His recommendations were given added emphasis by the findings of Project East River, which also urged that "a study should be made of the cost and feasibility of a comprehensive shelter program to provide a reasonable level of protection for those within vulnerable urban districts."

Val Peterson, shortly after he became Administrator of FCDA

in 1953, endorsed the House Appropriations Committee's refusal to vote funds for a mass-shelter program. He favored individual and family-type shelters, stating that his agency was "embarked upon a program to encourage the use of such shelters by individuals and families in our target areas."

But by 1956, when the House Military Operations Subcommittee, of which the writer is chairman, began its civil-defense investigations, Administrator Peterson had completely changed his views and upheld his predecessor's recommendations for public shelters as "sensible plans." He indicated that if he had to judge who was right, he "would be inclined to go along with Governor Caldwell rather than the Appropriations Committee." Nonetheless, Peterson indicated to our Committee that he favored a policy of mass evacuation rather than shelters. Thus nearly three years after the development of the hydrogen bomb and with full knowledge of developments in long-range ballistic missile technology, the Civil Defense Administrator was pursuing a mass-evacuation policy while at the same time acknowledging the need for shelter construction. Although the feasibility of mass evacuation had not been demonstrated, Administrator Peterson insisted that "evacuation is a sound tactic until the day that the intercontinental ballistic missile eliminates warning time."

Outside the FCDA, more realistic appraisals of civil-defense requirements were turning increasingly toward further shelter investigations. The Naval Radiological Defense Laboratory delivered a notable report to our Committee, concluding that a workable civil-defense system might begin with shelters; without these, other civil-defense measures would be largely meaningless, in view of the nature of the new weapons and vastly improved weapon-delivery systems.

To see the problems of evacuation, one need only consider the traffic jam caused by any major sports event in one of our large cities. A few thousand automobiles can clog all the main thoroughfares and access roads. Any attempt to move hundreds of thousands of people out of our major metropolitan areas—particularly in a period of great crisis and possible panic—would lead to utter chaos and confusion.

On the other hand, evacuation as a concept may seem attractive to civil-defense planners mainly concerned with avoiding large expenditures of money. It can be sponsored as a general approach to the problem without getting down to the hard facts of making it work, whereas if one recommends the construction of shelters, it becomes immediately apparent that large sums of money will be required. In fact, the Navy's study characterized evacuation planning as "a cheap substitute for atomic shelter."

The 1955 Project East River Review Committee likewise had determined that mass evacuation would be an unmanageable task. It favored limited, or tactical, evacuation, combined with the use of shelters.

The Military Operations Subcommittee took account of these findings in its report. Its recommendations called for a complete redrafting of legislation, affirming the Constitutional responsibility of the Federal Government for civil defense as an integral part of the national defense, while at the same time recognizing the vital supporting role of the states and localities. Among its specific proposals were: that all civil-defense functions be vested in a single new Department of Civil Defense; that this new agency formulate a national master plan for civil defense, based on public-shelter construction; that the secretary of the new department have statutory authority to carry out preparations to minimize the effects of any enemy attack upon the national economy and the people of the United States; that the secretary have vast emergency authority for action in case of an imminent or actual attack; and that the role of the military forces in civil defense be clearly defined.

At the beginning of the Eighty-fifth Congress, on January 7, 1957, the writer introduced in the House of Representatives a comprehensive civil-defense bill (H. R. 2125) drafted in accordance with the recommendations of our 1956 report. Subsequently every member of the Subcommittee and several other members of Congress introduced identical bills, and in February and March, 1957, the Subcommittee considered these bills and related legislation in public hearings.

During 1958 further civil-defense hearings were conducted by the Military Operations Subcommittee in connection with the Nevada bomb-shelter tests and the civil-defense reorganization plan submitted by the President. These hearings brought to light two outstanding new analyses of civil defense, one by the Operations Research Office of Johns Hopkins University and the other by the Rand Corporation.

The director of the Johns Hopkins studies, Ellis A. Johnson, listed civil defense as one of the three basic elements of national defense against a thermonuclear attack, the other two being military interception of the attack (e.g., by antimissile defenses) and military retaliation. He emphasized that the main deterrent to a possible attack upon the United States would continue to be our strategic attack forces, but he noted that air defenses and civil-defense measures could add to this deterrent by reducing the probable effects of such an attack. Thus these defenses would be important strategic factors, for they would make any attack on this country more costly for the enemy, both in terms of losses suffered by the attacking forces and in terms of the level of attack required to achieve a given degree of destruction.

The Rand Corporation's analysis, entitled "Report of a Study of Non-Military Defense," developed these principal findings: (1) nonmilitary measures could greatly reduce the effects of an enemy attack; (2) such measures could be prepared at a modest cost by reorientation of present programs and proper management of existing national resources; and (3) certain long-term nonmilitary defense plans, if initiated promptly, would develop invaluable preparedness for the United States. These would include inexpensive fallout protection for people outside blast areas, blast shelters, strategic or tactical evacuation if sufficient warning is available, measures to contain strontium 90 and cope with long-term radiation hazards, steps to provide a food supply after the attack, and so on.

These findings by the Rand Corporation, as well as recent studies of other organizations, have projected civil defense as a valuable component of our strategic deterrent strength and as an indispensable mechanism of national survival.

The simple truth that the Subcommittee has been endeavoring to make known is this: Although civil defense is a difficult task, it is not an impossible one, and the potential benefits are extremely important. Moreover, the costs are not unreasonable when considered in the context of our total expenditures for national security.

Civil Defense and Military Strategy

A further consideration of utmost importance goes to the role of civil-defense preparedness in strategic planning and cold-war diplomacy. What part does civil defense have in our general thesis of massive retaliation as a deterrent to war?

We must consider the possibility of extremely provocative action against us or our allies—but not direct attack on the United States—by the Soviet Union. What action would we be prepared to take in that event? If our civil defenses were no stronger than they are today, a decision to launch a massive retaliatory assault against the Soviet Union might result in the loss of 50 million or 100 million American lives in the counterattack, even if our strike forces substantially reduced the Soviet retaliatory capability. (If the Soviet Union should launch the first strike—which is more probable—the number of American casualties might exceed 100 million.) Consequently one must ask whether the United States would ever be willing to carry out its massive retaliation doctrine in any situation short of a direct massive assault against the American homeland.

This is not a pleasant question to consider, for it carries far-reaching implications with respect to our entire system of collective security for the free world. It not only raises issues as to the reliability of the United States as a partner in collective agreements but it goes to the question of whether the Soviet Union or her satellites will actually be deterred from encroaching on United States interests anywhere in the world.

A fundamental problem in discussing broad strategic considerations of this sort is a basic unwillingness on the part of Americans to look beyond the initial phase of a possible future war. Such myopia, unfortunately, extends to some of our highest military and civilian officials. As one military analyst has put it, "You can't get money programmed for a screwdriver today unless you can prove it would be used during the first 12 hours of an all-out war!"

To a certain extent, this attitude is understandable. Because our military effort is geared to the all-important desire to deter war, anything not contributing directly to our deterrent force is considered nonessential. If our deterrent force does not fulfill its mission, *i.e.*, if all-out war occurs, our primary military policy will have failed.

Given the possibility that our deterrent force may not in fact prevent an all-out war, there has been a tendency to throw up our collective hands in despair, refusing to contemplate or consider possible means of coping with the terrible effects of modern weapons.

Public awareness of our civil-defense needs has been stifled in the past by unreasonable restrictions on information relating to the effects of these weapons. Although great stocks of new weapons have been developed by the military and the Atomic Energy Commission, little information about their effects has been made available to the public or to the civil-defense workers and planners at state and local levels. In some categories of effects, notably fallout radiation, even the Federal Civil Defense Administration has had only a belated awareness or understanding. One of the major contributions to this situation has been the tendency of the Atomic Energy Commission to play down or understate the effects of nuclear weapons, including the possibly harmful effects of weapon testing.

As more facts have become known and as Congressional committees and various study groups have undertaken to explore the problems, the people are becoming more aware of our civil-defense needs. The nation seems to be concerning itself more and more with the requirements dictated by the changed circumstances of today. It is groping its way out of the primitive civil-defense concepts developed in World War II and reflected in the 1950 Act.

This is not to suggest that a concerted effort is now under way, but during 1958 there were certain manifestations of increased Federal concern. The Administration consolidated the Office of Defense Mobilization and the Federal Civil Defense Administration to form the new Office of Civil and Defense Mobilization (OCDM) within the Executive Office of the President; a Federal shelter policy was proclaimed; and Congress amended the Federal Civil Defense Act of 1950 to permit a somewhat expanded Federal role in future civil-defense preparations.

However, the OCDM's "National Shelter Policy"—not yet supported by Federal funds—falls short of the comprehensive construction program proposed by our Subcommittee. It merely provides for the development and construction of a limited number of prototype shelters for the guidance of state and local civil-defense authorities. It in no way represents the beginning of a national shelter-construction effort.

The 1958 amendments to the Federal Civil Defense Act made civil defense a "joint" responsibility of the Federal Government and the states, rather than a responsibility "vested primarily in the several states and their political subdivisions." This change in the declaration of policy, however, will have little meaning unless direct action is taken to expand the Federal effort. Nor will the other legislative changes have any effect unless the

Executive Branch gives positive and substantial support to civil defense.

Increased public awareness of civil-defense requirements was evidenced by a study undertaken by the American Medical Association under contract with the OCDM. This study, dealing with planning for medical care in the event of a national emergency, recognized some of the basic problems that must be solved. Without attempting to judge its technical merits from the medical standpoint, one can say that the AMA study represents a decided improvement in the very important area of civil-defense attitudes: what people think can be done and what a responsible and informed professional group believes we should be doing.

Federal Action Required

Despite these indications of increased national concern, action has been almost totally lacking. Federal pronouncements and changes in legislative policy have not been followed by specific steps to improve our civil-defense posture substantially. Demands for specific steps usually have been shunted aside on grounds that the Federal Government could not afford the outlays required. Yet between 1950 and 1958 the Federal Government doled out nearly half a billion dollars—$490 million, to be precise—for piecemeal civil-defense measures. Properly applied, these funds could have bought us at least the beginning of a realistic civil-defense program. As a minimum, we should have arrived at a clearly defined statement of civil-defense objectives and a planned effort to meet those objectives.

Today we still have very little understanding of the dimensions of civil defense in the age of thermonuclear weapons: how to warn 180 million Americans before intercontinental ballistic missiles begin falling on our cities; how best to provide essential shelter; how to incorporate protective features in our

industrial facilities (above ground as well as underground); how
to care for surviving casualties numbering in the tens of millions;
how to feed and otherwise care for our surviving population;
how to restore indispensable facilities and services; how to decontaminate land and facilities; how to preserve and ensure a
framework of government; how best to distribute and manage
surviving resources; how to restore our economy after the attack
—in short, the tasks of survival.

Certain things could be provided immediately, without a
great deal of advance planning and without large monetary
outlays. These include warning facilities, communications, radiological monitoring devices, emergency food, clothing, and medical supplies, and protection of existing stockpiles of strategic
materials.

In addition to a warning network, which is now partly built,
we must have communications facilities which will enable us to
keep the entire nation linked together even under the most
crushing circumstances. Individuals and families must not feel
isolated or alone, and a cooperative effort to survive must be
assured. Radiological monitoring equipment must be readily
available throughout the country, so that those in relatively un-
contaminated areas will know they can move about and those
in more hazardous areas will know they must stay sheltered.
Stocks of emergency medical supplies must be expanded, and
steps must be taken to apply our vast Federally-owned agri-
cultural surpluses to potential civil-defense purposes. In like
manner, our Federal stockpiles of critical and strategic raw
materials must be reoriented for their protection and early avail-
ability to meet civilian requirements in a post-attack situation.

Such tasks could be accomplished in a relatively short time
and at only a modest fraction of our annual outlays for military
measures. Other civil-defense measures, including the construction of fallout shelters or, preferably, blast shelters, will require
more time and larger expenditures by the Federal Government.
Further responsibilities must be accepted by the state and local
governments, within the framework of the national program,

and individual citizens throughout the country must be brought directly into the program.

Some Western countries already have trained large segments of their populations in civil-defense measures and have formed highly organized civil-defense corps. These include Great Britain, the Netherlands, Belgium, and the Scandinavian countries. In Denmark all private structures built after 1950 have been required to include reasonably secure shelters, and all persons between the ages of 16 and 65 are subject to conscription for service in the civil-defense corps.

The Soviet Union appears to have the most advanced program of indoctrination and training in civil defense of any country in the world. During World War II virtually its entire population was trained in civil defense, and within recent years new programs and modern techniques have been instituted for large segments of the population.

The essential question facing us is whether the American people are willing to prepare for the consequences of a nuclear attack on this country. This goes to the fundamental proposition of looking beyond the first phase of a possible large-scale war. It involves the long and arduous task of picking up the pieces after the noble charge into battle is over.

As unpleasant as the civil-defense chore may seem, its purpose is basically to preserve the peace. To be prepared to withstand the blow of a potential enemy is the best guarantee against such a blow. In the long term, civil defense must be considered a part of our total national preparedness effort. Until a workable international disarmament arrangement is achieved, we must continue our efforts not only to deter a possible enemy attack but also to reduce the impact such an attack would have on our country. As long as there is a danger of armed attack against the United States, civil defense—like our active military forces—will remain an essential requirement for the safety and welfare of the American people.

10

ARTHUR H. ROSENFELD

Detection of Bomb Tests

Ever since the first atomic bomb there has been a group of Americans, particularly scientists, who have sought to stop the development of a nuclear arms race by working for an international agreement to ban the testing of weapons. Up to the time that this is written, their efforts have been futile.

Shortly after World War II the Western nations put forth the Baruch plan for the control of atomic energy. It was doomed to wither because the Soviet Union determined to develop its own nuclear power. After the Russians succeeded in producing a bomb in 1949, and the United States (and of course the U.S.S.R. also) decided that they must develop a weapon even more terrible than the fission bomb, thoughtful Americans again urged their government to put a brake on weapon testing. Their reasoning was well expressed by Vannevar Bush, who went to Secretary of State Dean Acheson in the summer of 1952 to urge that the impending test of the first H-bomb be called off. He made his plea for "two primary reasons": first, because in exploding this new bomb the United States would have to carry the responsibility of "our entry into a very disagreeable type of world," and secondly, because he believed that it would destroy the possibility of reaching an agreement with Russia to stop the testing of nuclear weapons.

By that time, however, the United States Government was hardened by several years' experience with the cold war, and it reluctantly dismissed the proposal as impractical.

The awakening of serious public interest in a bomb-test ban had to wait until the explosion of the fission-fusion-fission bomb on March 1, 1954. The fate of the unlucky crew of the *Lucky Dragon* and of the irradiated Marshall Islanders, and the AEC's admission (11 months later!) that the explosion had produced unprecedented fallout, made plain that H-bomb tests were hard to hide, and that their control could logically be considered separately from the deadlocked UN negotiations on general arms limitation.

The arguments for seeking a limited agreement to ban only the testing of H-bombs were summed up at the time by David R. Inglis, chairman of the Committee on Arms Control of the Federation of American Scientists, in an article in the *Bulletin of the Atomic Scientists*. Its main points were: that there was a reasonable chance such an agreement might be acceptable to both sides, that it could pave the way to a more ambitious arms-limitation agreement, and that it would prevent the development of H-bombs by other nations, with the possibility that some irrational statesman sometime might "make the fatal mistake" that would destroy civilization. Note that fallout was not mentioned in these arguments: scientists have seldom advanced fallout alone as the primary reason for ending nuclear testing.

Neither the Soviet nor the United States Government took this proposal seriously enough to study how it might be implemented. Two years later, during the 1956 Presidential campaign, President Eisenhower still dismissed the idea almost as firmly as Adlai Stevenson urged it. Yet within two more years (perhaps with a little push from Linus Pauling and from the Killian Committee) the same United States Administration proposed to ban the testing not only of H-bombs but of all nuclear devices! Negotiations for a general agreement to stop tests finally began in 1958. They would have done the world more good if they had been undertaken when Bush urged them in 1952.

Detection of Nuclear Explosions

After an exchange of notes between the United States and the U.S.S.R., experts from both sides settled down at Geneva in the summer of 1958 to consider the technical questions involved. Present were scientists from the United States, Great Britain, Canada, and France, and their counterparts from the U.S.S.R., Poland, Czechoslovakia, and Rumania. The conference made an inauspicious beginning, but after seven weeks of discussions it arrived at unprecedented agreement on the main question: Could a practical system be set up for detecting and identifying nuclear explosions?

Before we can discuss the technical problems, we must review some of the facts about such explosions. As earlier chapters have pointed out, the size of a nuclear explosion is measured in terms of its equivalent in tons of TNT. A thousand tons is called a kiloton, and a million tons a megaton. The smallest nuclear bomb is believed to "yield" about one kiloton. The table below lists some comparisons.

CHEMICAL EXPLOSION		NUCLEAR EXPLOSION	
Tons of TNT		"Yield"	
1	World War II Blockbuster	?	Nuclear "Bazooka" *
1,000	Large World War II Air Raid	1 kiloton	"Small" Tactical Weapon
100,000		100 kilotons	"Large" Fission Bomb
2,000,000	Total of World War II Raids	2 megatons	"Small" H-bomb

* In the spring of 1959 the AEC announced that it had successfully tested a nuclear weapon of unprecedentedly low yield which could be handled by a two-man bazooka team and had the striking power "of a World War II bomber."

The problem of detecting and identifying a nuclear explosion depends not only on its size but also on where it takes place: (1) at the surface of the earth (on the ground or in the air), (2) underground, or (3) in outer space. Let us consider the three cases separately.

Surface Tests. A nuclear explosion above ground can be seen and heard and produces a telltale fallout. The acoustic signal from an explosion as small as one kiloton can be "heard" and identified by instruments as far as 1,000 miles away. Thus a surface test can easily be detected and identified as a nuclear explosion. There is now general agreement that a ban of surface tests would be practicable and desirable.

Underground Tests. Because of the objectionable features of surface tests, particularly fallout, David Griggs and Edward Teller suggested in 1956 that it might be less hazardous, cheaper, and more reliable to test nuclear weapons underground. The first such test was conducted on September 19, 1957, in a shaft 900 feet below the surface of a mesa in the Nevada Proving Grounds. This 1.7-kiloton shot, called "Rainier," was a great success. It showed that underground testing was practical, and thus opened the way to a form of testing which would eliminate fallout and could be conducted in any kind of weather. The success of the experiment also gave impetus to "Project Ploughshare"—the study of nonmilitary applications of nuclear explosions.

The Rainier shot turned out to be hard to detect from a distance, and almost impossible to identify as a nuclear explosion by the usual methods. Had the AEC chosen to try to hide it, an inspection team would have had an extremely hard time proving that it had taken place. To see why, let us examine the shot and its effects in more detail.

The underground shaft where the bomb lay was curved, so that the explosion collapsed the opening and sealed itself in. There was no eruption through the surface of the mountain, and almost all the radioactivity was trapped in a sphere of fused rock 60 feet in diameter. The detonation produced small earthquake waves which were detected by some seismic stations thousands of miles away (though the AEC at first announced that they had been picked up only by a few stations close by). But these waves were merely suspicious: they looked somewhat different from natural earthquake waves but not conclusively different. So we come face to face with the difference between "detection" and "identification." It is one thing to detect a signal, but quite another to prove what the signal means.

Can seismographs distinguish an explosion from other disturbances of the earth? We must reckon first of all with the normal small vibrations ("microseisms") which sensitive seismographs record as background "noise." The earth is constantly shaking from various impacts—ocean storms, local winds, the rumble of trains and factories, and so forth. This "noise" will drown the characteristic signal of an underground explosion at some distance from the site, where the signal has weakened. The explosion signal must be several times larger than the noise if it is to be distinguished from a natural earthquake (see Figure 18). At a good inland station on a quiet day the noise may be as low as one millimicron (1.0 on the scale of Figure 19). At the bottom of a hole in the earth several thousand feet deep, the seismic noise may be one tenth that at the surface. Thus a seismograph is more effective in detection if it is buried some distance below ground level.

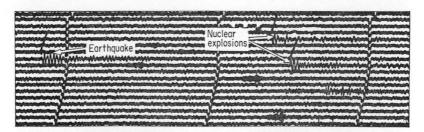

FIG. 18. Seismograph record showing that waves from underground explosions are very similar to those produced by a natural earthquake. At the right are signals from two nuclear explosions in a United States test series in the summer of 1958. Within the hour this seismograph, in Fairbanks, Alaska, picked up a third signal (left) which is thought to be from an earthquake but could have come from a Russian bomb test. (The picture is reproduced with permission from an article by J. Carson Mark in *Nucleonics*, August, 1959.)

The vibrations from an explosion fortunately have a distinctive feature which makes it possible to differentiate them from a true earthquake. An earthquake is a relatively slow shearing of rock, whereas a nuclear explosion produces a sudden compression. Both set up compression waves in the earth, but the earthquake waves tend to form a cloverleaf pattern with, say, the north-and-south leaves showing a direction of first motion away from the quake, and the east-and-west leaves moving initially toward the quake. An explosion, on the other hand, sets up an outward earth movement in *all* directions. So the best way to distinguish an explosion from a natural earthquake is to space seismic stations closely enough so that about five of them can detect the direction of first motion.

How close is "close enough"? This depends in part, as we have just seen, on the size of the signal—that is, on the distance it will travel before the direction of first motion is lost in the background noise. But the detection distance is also governed by a peculiar skipping characteristic of all earthquake signals. Because the various layers of the earth transmit sound (*i.e.*, compression waves) at different speeds, a seismic disturbance is focused and reflected back to the surface in periodic fashion (see Figure 19). The result is a series of "skip" zones, about 2,000 kilometers (1,250 miles) apart, where the signal is not detectable; each skip zone is about 1,000 kilometers long. Because the signal is weaker at each skip, ideally the stations should be spaced closely enough so that five of them are inside the first skip from any point, *i.e.*, within a few hundred miles from the explosion. At this distance they could identify "small" underground explosions down to somewhere between one and ten kilotons.

We can see now how difficult it would be to verify such an explosion if the testing experts tried to hide it. Suppose that a nuclear bomb is buried in an area where there are frequent earthquakes. Circuits can be arranged so that an innocent earthquake will trigger the explosion. After the bomb has been planted, one closes the shaft or tunnel, waits a few months until

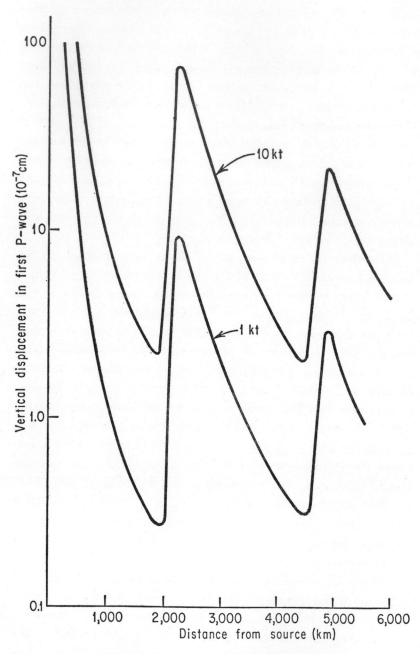

FIG. 19. Chart showing "skip" zones where earthquake signals diminish in amplitude. (This illustration also is from J. Carson Mark's article in *Nucleonics*.)

rain, snow, and vegetation obliterate all traces of the digging, and then turns on the triggering circuits.

When an earthquake sets off the bomb, the inspection team may notice something fishy in the tracings on its seismographs. The inspectors will raise the question of a nuclear test, but those who have conducted the secret test will challenge them to "prove it!" With a carefully designed inspection system, it could be done, but it might be hard.

A network of seismic stations such as the Geneva experts proposed would often not be able to narrow down the epicenter of the disturbance to much better than an area five miles in radius. (If the triggering earthquake that set off the explosion was within five miles of the bomb, it might effectively mask the seismic signals.) So the inspectors would have an area of some 100 square miles to comb for signs of the bomb shaft. They might get an approximate fix on the bomb site by using test explosions of TNT and making geological studies of the area. After many man-years of work, the inspectors might succeed pretty well in pinpointing the explosion site. They would then start drilling for the radioactive pocket underground, but they would still have to hit a spot only about 100 feet in diameter!

All this is what is meant by "on-site inspections." Both the United States and the U.S.S.R. agreed that they are a necessary element of any agreement to police underground tests, but they disagreed on how many inspections per year would be needed.

Tests in Space. I have taken up the matter of underground tests in considerable detail because they constitute the chief problem. A more effective, but also more difficult, way to conceal nuclear bomb tests would be to explode the bombs in "outer" space (whatever "outer" means). Such explosions could be made arbitrarily hard to detect and impossible to identify. They will be feasible, however, only when completely dependable rockets and instruments have been developed.

Let us see how such a test might be carried out with a rocket such as the Russian Lunik I, which took an 800-pound payload away from the earth's pull. Suppose that its 800 pounds of in-

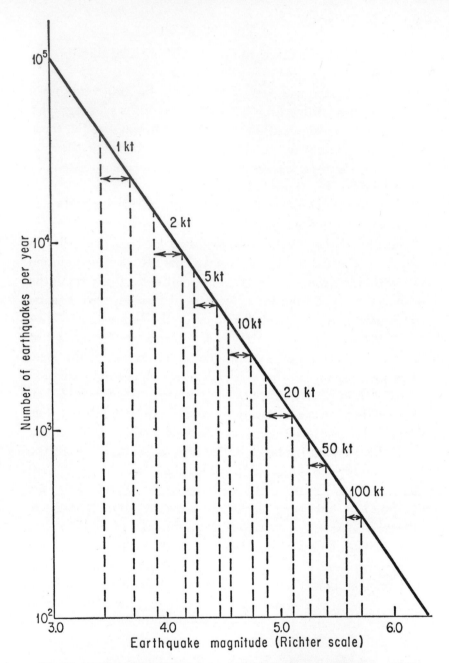

FIG. 20. Annual rates of earthquakes according to magnitude, with their explosion equivalents in kilotons. For example, each year there are about 1,000 earthquakes in the world equivalent to a 20-kiloton explosion, it is estimated. The estimates are based on United States test explosions underground in Nevada in the fall of 1956 and on other data. (From J. Carson Mark's article in *Nucleonics*.)

struments were replaced by a 500-pound nuclear bomb, 300 pounds of sensing instruments, and a 20-pound radio transmitter. After the rocket had flown a few million miles away from the earth, radio signals from the control station on earth could release the instrument package and shortly afterward trigger the bomb. The instruments would radio back to the observers crucial information about the test explosion—its energy, etc.

How could inspectors detect such a test? Stations on the earth itself would not have much chance. The Geneva experts briefly considered the possibility of maintaining a network of several detection satellites, equipped with appropriate instruments. But they did not try to estimate how well these space stations would work, partly because more information is needed about how much interfering "noise" there would be from cosmic rays in space. Probably it will be possible in a few years to send up satellites with instruments good enough to detect megaton tests even millions of miles away, but it looks almost impossible to detect kiloton explosions just beyond the moon.

My opinion is that the only satisfactory way to control testing in space would be by inspection of rocket launchings. At all events, rocket-borne tests in space probably will not be practical for a few years anyway. The problem of banning such tests can be by-passed for the time being or left to year-to-year agreements. I believe that we should concentrate on the main immediate problem of controlling testing on the earth, where some sort of control system *is* practical.

Conclusions of the Technical Conference

The Geneva scientists devoted themselves to this central question, and they came to the conclusion that it was practical to detect terrestrial tests of nuclear weapons down to "small" explosions between one and five kilotons. A noteworthy feature of their sessions was the spirit of the discussions. There was an encouraging amount of give-and-take on the technical questions. One example of this was the Russians' yielding on a sticky point about the importance of the "skip" region. The Russians at first denied that such a region existed, and then claimed that it amounted to only 200 kilometers. Nikolai N. Semyonov, Nobel laureate chemist in the Russian delegation, argued the point at length with Sir Edward Bullard, the well-known English geophysicist. When they failed to resolve their differences, the chief Russian seismologist, Dr. Sadovski, interposed: "We are standing on the position that was adopted by Professor Semyonov, undoubtedly, but we agree that the question is far from being as simple as he has now stated here. . . . I am more inclined to agree with Professor Bullard than with what Nikolai Nikolayevitch [Semyonov] has just said."

This incident, as well as others, showed that the working scientists on the Russian team were quite open-minded and willing to come to sound technical conclusions.

The conference agreed that, within certain limitations, it was technically feasible to set up "a workable and effective control system for the detection of violations of an agreement on the world-wide cessation of nuclear weapons tests." It suggested a combination of acoustic, hydroacoustic, seismic, and radiation-detection methods, and it went on to propose a world-wide network of about 180 control posts, spaced about 1,000 miles apart in most regions and about 600 miles apart in areas of earthquake activity. There would be roughly 24 stations in North America, 6 in Europe, 37 in Asia, 7 in Australia, 16 in South America, 16 in Africa, and 4 in Antarctica, with 60 more on islands and ships. In addition, regular flights of aircraft along north-south routes over the oceans would collect samples of air for measurements of radioactivity.

The conference observed that the control posts would be concerned to a large extent with watching for underground explosions, recognized as "one of the most difficult" problems. It proposed that about 30 experts "with various qualifications and fields of specialization" should staff each control post. Unfortunately it expressed no agreement as to how many of these 30 should be nationals of the country involved and how many foreigners. The report continued:

> When the control posts detect an event which cannot be identified by the international control organ and which could be suspected of being a nuclear explosion, the international control organ can send an inspection group to the site of this event to determine whether a nuclear explosion had taken place or not. The group would be provided with equipment and apparatus appropriate to its task in each case. The inspection group would forward a report on the investigation it had carried out to the international control organ, and to the government of the country on the territory of which the investigation was made in such a manner as may be considered appropriate by governments.

The proposed system, said the report, would have the following effectiveness:

> (a) Good probability of detecting and identifying nuclear explosions of yields down to about one kiloton, taking place on the surface of the earth and up to ten kilometers altitude, and good probability of detecting, but not always of identifying, explosions taking place at altitudes from ten to 50 kilometers.
> (b) Good probability of detecting nuclear explosions of one kiloton yield set off deep in the ocean.

Thus we see that the logical extension in 1960 of the H-bomb testing ban proposed in 1952 to 1956 is a ban of *all surface tests*. Both sides agree that the surface ban can easily be monitored.

The report went on to discuss the thornier problem of underground tests, and it concluded that there was:

> (c) Good probability of recording seismic signals from deep underground nuclear explosions . . . equivalent to one kiloton and above. [However] along with the observation of signals of possible underground explosions, the control posts would record at the same time a considerable number of similar signals from natural earthquakes. Although, with the present state of knowl-

edge and techniques, the network of control posts would be unable to distinguish the signals of underground explosions from those of some earthquakes, it could identify as being of natural origin about 90 per cent of the continental earthquakes whose signals are equivalent to five kilotons, and a small percentage of continental earthquakes equivalent to one kiloton. It has been estimated . . . that the number of earthquakes which would be indistinguishable . . . from deep underground explosions of about five kilotons yield could be . . . from 20 to 100 a year. Those unidentified events that could be suspected of being nuclear explosions would be inspected [on site].

It is important to distinguish between what the Geneva report called "good" probability of detecting each individual test and what I would call "reasonable" probability of detecting at least one test in a series. Let us assume that there are between 2,000 and 10,000 earthquakes per year that look like one-kiloton explosions (100 times the number estimated to look like five-kiloton tests). This does not mean that we would necessarily have to make 2,000 to 10,000 inspections. With a few hundred inspections of suspicious signals we might have a "reasonable" probability—perhaps 10 per cent—of detecting a single small underground test. If a nation made a series of five such tests, there would be nearly a 50 per cent chance of catching one in the series. This might well be a sufficient deterrent against trying secret tests.

Unfortunately, the Geneva estimate of the number of difficult-to-detect tests was slightly overoptimistic, as further study showed.

The Berkner Study

Although the Geneva experts did a magnificent job, it is hardly to be expected that in the space of seven weeks they should have explored every difficulty and come up with a perfect plan invulnerable to criticisms by Monday-morning quarterbacks. In fact, technical and other objections quickly developed. The conferees had had to base their thinking on just one underground test—the Rainier shot. The Western delegates suggested that the proposed network be tested by experimental shots, particularly to see if an explosion could be concealed by cushioning it, but the Russians rejected the suggestion and the Western group gave in. New data soon showed that the Western doubts were justified.

In response to the feeling of many that the Geneva report left some important questions unanswered, the President's Science Advisory Committee appointed a committee of distinguished American scientists to study the feasibility of improving the Geneva inspection system. The committee, under the chairmanship of Lloyd Berkner, president of Associated Universities, started its work in the fall of 1958, and it had the advantage of information from further underground explosions detonated during the "Hardtack" series of tests hurriedly carried out that fall in Nevada.

From the new data, the Berkner committee concluded that it was "more difficult to identify underground explosions than had previously been believed." The committee then set out to find ways to patch up the proposed inspection system. But before it could arrive at any opinion on whether this would be difficult, the Administration decided to warn the public of the danger of a test-ban agreement on the basis of the Geneva plan. It issued a press release which *The New York Times* published on January 6, 1959, under the headline: U.S. SEES LOOPHOLE IN ATOM BAN PLAN. The story said that the seismic signals from explosions were smaller and the detection system less effective than had been anticipated, so that the number of earthquakes indistinguishable from a five-kiloton explosion, for example, would be ten or more times what the Geneva conference had estimated.

When the release was published, diplomatic representatives of the nuclear powers were in Geneva trying to draft an agreement on banning nuclear tests. The Russians were furious at the United States announcement, taking it to be an effort to sabotage the talks. Their indignation would have been received with more understanding if they had not refused to consider the new data turned up by the Berkner committee. However, many Westerners also were perturbed at the Government's announcement, which certainly emphasized difficulty rather than hope. Senator Hubert Humphrey objected to the statement in a speech on the floor of the Senate:

> This does not mean that the data prove that detection of nuclear tests has now become so difficult that, to quote again from a prominent periodical, "the chances of deception are so great as to be a major risk to survival" because "the real minimum underground blast that could be fully detected was about 20 kilotons." This conclusion not only is invalid. It is factually incorrect and completely misleading. . . .
>
> I understand that there are several promising techniques to improve the capabilities without increasing the size of the system recommended at Geneva. These include: building better instruments, devising ways to blot out background noise, placing seismographs deep in the earth, substantially increasing the number of seismographs at each control post over the number provided for in the Geneva Report, utilization of additional methods to distinguish earthquake signals from nuclear explosions other than the determination of first motion, and use of unmanned seismographs to augment the Geneva system. Another obvious improvement is to increase the number of manned control posts. The President's Science Advisory Committee is continuing to study how the control system might be improved. I hope and urge that its report be made public.

The Berkner report was finally released on June 12, 1959. It said that on the basis of the Hardtack tests the number of earthquakes per year that could not be distinguished from a five-kiloton explosion by the Geneva network was 1,500 instead of 20 to 100, as the Geneva conference had estimated. However, with improvements in the network which were already technically feasible, the ambiguous number could be reduced from

1,500 to 300. And if the Geneva network were augmented with deep, unmanned seismic stations spaced about 100 miles apart in the earthquake areas of the world, the system might be able to identify all but about 2 per cent of the natural earthquakes as small as the equivalent of one kiloton. The report went on to suggest experiments to test the seismic detection system under various conditions, including different rock types and deliberate attempts to cushion an explosion, which could reduce the seismic signal by a factor of ten or possibly much more than ten. I would interpret the findings, in informal language, as follows:

1. We cannot tell how well the network will work until we install at least some of the stations and start experimenting. There is an excellent chance that with any reasonable cooperation from the Russians we can construct a network good down to about ten kilotons, with no major changes from the Geneva proposal. To get down to one kiloton will probably take more closely spaced stations or improvements in seismology or both.

2. Only experiment can tell whether cushioning is an effective way to hide tests. We could have the answer in less than a year. Even if cushioning turned out to be very effective, that would not necessarily mean that *no* control of tests was possible; we might just have to settle for a more modest agreement.

In summary, if we are serious about a ban we must do more than negotiate and issue press releases. We must experiment with detection techniques and sponsor basic research in seismology. We must devote energy, money, and imagination to the problem. Unilateral efforts by the West can solve many of the technical problems, but it will take East-West cooperation to set up a trustworthy control system.

Compromise Proposals

The Geneva experts proposed an absolute ban on all nuclear weapon testing. This would be most desirable if we had a detection system capable of detecting all tests of military significance. Such an agreement would hinder any further development of weapons by the present nuclear powers and could stop the making of A-bombs by new nations. Of course to achieve the latter objective the signatory countries would have to depend on moral, political, and economic pressures, because a small nation determined to develop atomic weapons could not be deterred merely by the nuclear powers' threat to resume their own testing.

Although the West's and East's scientific experts agreed that an absolute ban was feasible, the diplomats who went to Geneva to negotiate an agreement have been unable to do so up to this writing (December, 1959). The Russians have refused to improve the network as the Berkner report suggests, or to discuss what to do if the network fails (as it probably would) to perform as advertised. In addition, the Russians have been very reluctant to grant two demands which the West considers important: (1) that the control posts be staffed largely by persons who are not nationals of the country in which the posts are located, and (2) that frequent on-site inspections be allowed. These positions seem to derive from the Russians' extreme xenophobia and suspiciousness about the possibility of the network being used as a pretext for espionage in their country.

Would it make sense to try to break the impasse by seeking a more limited type of agreement or by restricting our concern to explosions of five kilotons and up? Let us see what might be achieved, for example, if the number of on-site inspections were reduced to a minimum. It seems to me that on this point the Russian position is reasonable. On-site inspections would often involve large-scale drilling operations, would be tedious and expensive, and would engage hundreds of workers; it would be better to put the funds and personnel into establishing more stations, for this would permanently improve the detection system, whereas an on-site inspection one year is of no help for the next.

Suppose the number of on-site inspections in the Soviet Union were limited to two each year, and similarly two each year in

China. Of the 300 earthquakes in the world each year that are indistinguishable from five-kiloton explosions (according to the Berkner report), perhaps 30 occur in the territories of these two countries. If the control agency could make on-site inspections of four out of 30 suspicious events (some of which might be underground tests), it would have a 13 per cent chance of discovering an individual bomb test. This is probably good enough to deter a nation from secret testing at the five-kiloton level or higher—certainly from conducting series of such tests.

Is a detection threshold of five kilotons low enough to make a ban on all testing workable? Probably not; a nation would soon repudiate the agreement if it suspected that any party to the agreement was cheating by conducting smaller tests. But if the threshold could be reduced to one kiloton, the military advantage that a nation might gain by secret testing below this level might be small enough to be outweighed by the advantages of a general control agreement.

Reliable detection down to one kiloton is still only a hope. But it is my personal belief that we can safely propose a progressive program which makes sense and which the Russians might find acceptable.

The Russians, on the one hand, want an absolute ban on all tests, but they want to police it with a network which, even if improved according to the Berkner committee's suggestions, probably cannot detect tests below ten kilotons. On the other hand, the Geneva experts felt that they should design a network which could deter tests down to one kiloton, and most Westerners still feel that a network *must* be that good if it is to be relied upon.

My personal suggestion for a compromise is to say to the Russians:

"1. We are not backing away from our stand at the Geneva technical conference. Let us both agree now that we shall stop all testing as soon as the network has been demonstrated to be capable of reliable control down to one kiloton, with an acceptable number of on-site inspections per year.

"2. Let us install the network immediately. This task will take a year or so. As a sign of good faith let us both conduct no more bomb tests during that time. (There will be no way of checking on one another, but let us take the risk for that relatively short time.) Let us also start unclassified experiments on both the detection and the cushioning of tests.

"3. Improvements in detection techniques and instruments that are developed while the network is being built should be incorporated in it. When the completed network is checked out, it may turn out to be capable of controlling tests down to one kiloton. In that case we will have followed the Geneva plan, right on schedule. If, as seems probable, the network does not work down to one kiloton, we shall have to improve it, perhaps by adding more stations. (This seems easier than to permit more on-site inspections.) Meanwhile we could discontinue all tests detectable by the network. This is far less satisfactory than an absolute ban, but it will give us valuable experience. It would also eliminate fallout, for all tests above ground are detectable and therefore would be discontinued."

This program follows the Geneva proposals, provides strong motivation for improving the control system, and even in its limited phases would establish the important principle of control of nuclear weapons. It would put severe obstacles in the way of more nations developing such weapons. Most important, it would be both a symbolic and a concrete step toward relaxing world tensions and ending the general arms race.

11 RALPH E. LAPP

Nuclear War

The magnitude of a nuclear war can be defined in terms of megatons. A modest attack, in these days of superbombs and large stockpiles, might be, say, 3,000 megatons; a big one would go over 10,000 megatons. The bombing would be concentrated within a very short time—perhaps a day or two if the nuclear explosives were delivered by manned bombers, a few hours if they were delivered by ballistic missiles. What would be the results of such an attack upon the continental United States?

A nation such as ours, with its immense land area (roughly three million square miles) might be thought able to absorb even a very large nuclear attack without being paralyzed. But the new weapons have radically changed all dimensions, because of (1) their range of destruction, (2) the biological hazards, and (3) the new time scale. It is almost impossible to assess the really revolutionary impact of the compression of time effected by the quick deliverability of modern explosives. In World War II Germany absorbed a total of almost two million tons of bombs and still was able to carry on war production. This weight of attack was spread over two years, however. Had Germany's population and industrial economy suffered equivalent damage in two nights rather than in two years, recovery would not have been possible.

This chapter will discuss the extent of destruction and the biological consequences of a hypothetical 3,000-megaton attack on the United States. No attempt will be made to assess the degree to which the nation could recuperate from such an attack, because this would depend upon many imponderables. The Rand Corporation's published "Report on a Study of Non-Military Defense" in 1958 concluded that the United States could sustain heavy nuclear damage and recover. But the Rand optimism was based on the assumption that the population could be sheltered properly; this implies a degree of preattack preparation and readiness that is lacking today. Herman Kahn, who spearheaded the Rand analysis, divided the United States into two countries: Country A, consisting of the large metropolitan complexes, presumably would be effectively knocked out by the attack, but Country B, the remaining portion, would survive to rebuild Country A and restore the nation to its prewar economy. This assumes that the level of attack would not be high enough to overwhelm the resources of Country B. It also assumes that the population would be prepared to escape the direct onslaught of a nuclear attack, to weather the fallout hazard, and then to repair the torn fabric of its society.

Rather than attempt a single-handed Rand analysis, I shall focus upon the weapon hazards and relate these specifically to personal, not national, survival.

The Targets

First, where will the weapons fall? It is not very realistic to suppose that they will be confined to their targets. With bombers battling their way in against determined defenses, the bombs may fall wide of their intended marks. Whereas in theory 50 per cent of the bombs might fall within 4,000 feet of the aiming points, in practice many might be dropped far outside this distance off target. And intercontinental ballistic missiles might be scattered over a tenfold wider area around the aiming point.

(These estimates are based on present capabilities; if we looked into the future, we would have to expect greater missile accuracy and bigger warheads.)

We can predict what the main targets will be. These targets call for large weapons. At the present time a manned bomber such as the B-52 carries a strategic weapon of some 20 megatons. It is prudent to assume that the Soviets have an equal capability. Given further weapon development, this strategic weapon can be doubled in explosive power. Present and planned long-range ballistic missiles have warheads ranging from under one megaton for Polaris, the submarine-launched missile, to a projected five megatons for heavier ICBMs. One can forecast conservatively that improvements in rocket fuels and in missile design, along with greater nuclear efficiency, should produce a ten-megaton ICBM warhead by the mid-1960's. I would not be surprised if continued testing evolved a much more powerful weapon.

The reason for emphasis upon bigger weapons is that the prime targets would be hard-to-destroy ICBM bases. The present Strategic Air Command bomber bases are soft, but we must think ahead to the time when missiles will be the military preference. ICBM bases will then consist of a complex of "hardened" underground installations capable of withstanding a peak overpressure of 100 pounds per square inch. This means that a ten-megaton explosive would have to hit within 1.3 miles of the missile chute to destroy the ICBM in its underground silo. The major ICBM bases are clustered west of the Mississippi River, but with the advent of the solid-fuel Minuteman missile, the retaliatory launch sites will be scattered throughout the United States, some in hardened sites, others on mobile platforms.

Because an enemy would have to knock out our retaliatory capability, he would concentrate his attack upon the strategic bases. Our cities do not represent prime targets, except as there are strategic bases in their vicinity. Factories, so intimately associated with metropolitan areas, are no longer a prime target, for in a missile blitzkrieg both sides would have to "fight out of

inventory." A nation's production capacity (typified by the De-
troit production line) no longer is the great deterrent to an
aggressor; what he must fear most is the readiness potential,
represented by missiles and aircraft and the nuclear weapons
already stockpiled. For this reason even the production facilities of the Atomic Energy Commission do not rank as prime
or secondary targets. Why worry about the Golden Goose when
it has already produced 10,000 eggs?

It would be highly desirable to divorce the prime targets in
the United States from the population-food areas, so that a
nuclear attack would not automatically spill over into the non-
military arena. As things are, the fact that our retaliatory bases
are located in the American heartland, together with the fact
that solid-fueled ballistic missiles may be moved anywhere,
allows an enemy little alternative but to strike at both military
and nonmilitary targets in the first blow. Whereas many of our
cities might be spared severe blast damage from all except off-
course bombs, others might suffer this direct damage because of
their proximity to strategic targets. All would be expected to
come within the range of serious radioactive fallout.

Fire and Blast

Before we consider the fallout, which probably would be the
greatest peril to the general population, we shall take up the
primary effects of nuclear weapons. As has already been explained, the temperature created in a nuclear explosion is vastly
higher than that produced by the detonation of TNT or a
similar chemical explosive. Assume that a ten-megaton nuclear
weapon is detonated at the earth's surface. It releases roughly
a third of its total energy in the form of heat and light. This
rapid outpouring of thermal energy heats the bomb material
and the surrounding air to temperatures exceeding those in the
mantle of the sun. The fireball grows quickly to a diameter of
three and a half miles.

In the first moments the fireball's internal temperature is in excess of millions of degrees Centigrade. Its surface temperature rises, then drops, then rises again, so that there is a double pulse of radiated heat. The first pulse lasts a tiny fraction of a second and consists of ultraviolet light. The second pulse pours out heat and light over a period of many seconds, reaching a maximum rate at three seconds. About two thirds of the fireball's heat radiation is emitted in ten seconds.

On a clear day when the visibility is about ten miles or more, this heat flash would produce second-degree burns (blistering the skin) on exposed persons out to a distance of 25 miles from the explosion. Third-degree burns (complete destruction of the skin) would be expected out to about 20 miles. Industrial haze, smog, or fog would shrink these ranges drastically. Some form of opaque covering that shielded the body from the direct rays of the fireball would give complete protection against burns. Eyes would be blinded if they looked directly at the fireball. The blink reflex and the natural tendency to look away might protect most people in the case of a bomb exploded near ground level, but these instinctive reactions might not cope with the solar-like flash from a bomb exploded at very high altitude.

We have been considering that the bomb would be a surface burst, but it is possible that an enemy might deliberately detonate a bomb at high altitude in order to maximize the heat effect. Some explosions might occur at high altitudes as a result of defensive interceptions of missiles. In the absence of air a nuclear explosion concentrates more energy in the heat flash. A ten-megaton burst in the thin atmosphere 30 miles above the earth's surface could send a searing wave of heat over an area of 5,000 square miles.

Combustibles within this area would be ignited by the flash. The flash of heat, plus the effects of blast, would start a multitude of small blazes. Under certain conditions these would fuse into large fires and ultimately might produce a "firestorm," the technical name of a massive fire in which air drawn toward the center of the burning area has a blow-torch effect and perpetuates the conflagration. Several firestorms were produced by the bombing of German cities with incendiaries, and one firestorm occurred after a fire raid on Tokyo. The atomic bombs created a firestorm at Hiroshima but not at Nagasaki. Some experts who have studied the phenomenon believe that firestorms would be an inevitable consequence of a megaton burst over a large American city. A team of three specialists testified at the 1959 hearings of the Subcommittee on Radiation of the Joint Committee on Atomic Energy: "It is no exaggeration to say that, after a nuclear attack, burn casualties [would] represent the most serious medical problem facing the nation."

The firestorm poses a vexing problem to civil-defense planners. Shelters would have to be provided with a built-in atmosphere (*i.e.*, an oxygen supply), for the holocaust would consume the available oxygen in the air. Naturally, shelters designed to withstand firestorms will be considerably more expensive than those aimed at protecting only against the radiation hazard.

After the heat flash, the next and most obvious effect of a megaton explosion is the blast wave. About half of the bomb's energy goes into blast. Directly under the bomb, the blast excavates a yawning crater. In the case of a ten-megaton bomb detonated over dry soil, the crater would be about 250 feet deep and half a mile wide. Some of the heavy debris would form a thick lip around the crater, and light material would be sucked up into the ascending fireball. In a zone around the crater, all conventional buildings and structures would be destroyed. This zone of complete demolition might be three miles in diameter —about the same width as that of the fireball. There would be no human survivors in this area, except possibly in strong, deep shelters.

The blast "overpressure" would be 100 pounds per square inch at 1.3 miles, 50 psi at 1.8 miles, 25 psi at 2.4 miles, 15 psi at 3.3 miles, 5 psi at 6.1 miles, 2.5 psi at slightly under 10 miles, and 1.5 psi at 14 miles. What does this mean in terms of building damage and human injury at the respective distances?

Too often even the experts talk loosely about areas of "complete devastation" without specifying what kind of building is used as the gauge or what sort of area is under consideration. Concrete structures will resist destruction more than wooden ones; in a densely built city area some buildings will be shielded by others.

Building damage is conventionally described in terms of four categories: A—virtually complete destruction, B—severe damage, perhaps not repairable, C—moderate to major damage, requiring considerable repairs, D—light damage requiring only minor repairs. Massive, multistory buildings of unusually strong construction would suffer A damage out to 2.5 miles, B to 3.5 miles, and C to a little over five miles. Less strongly built, reinforced-concrete structures with small window areas would exhibit A damage out to three miles, B to four miles, and C to six miles. Apartment houses with load-bearing walls of brick construction would show A damage out to a little more than four miles, B to 5.3 miles, and C to nine miles.

Wood-frame houses, such as crowd the landscape in many cities, are very vulnerable to blast, succumbing to a very small overpressure. One would expect such houses to be completely destroyed out to seven miles from the burst—over an area of 150 square miles. Grade B damage would extend to nine miles and C out to 12 miles from Ground Zero, or over an area of 450 square miles. This means that anything approximating a hit upon a metropolitan area (excepting the very large areas of New York and Los Angeles) would knock out almost all wood-frame housing. Basement shelters in such houses would not be very safe, for the debris would collapse into the cellar.

Minor blast damage, such as plaster-cracking and window-breaking, would extend to 100 miles or more from the explosion. Within 11 to 14 miles or so the flying shards of glass and masonry would be traveling fast enough to constitute dangerous missiles. People themselves might become "missiles"—by being picked up and thrown about violently by the blast wind. The technical experts call this effect "translation" or "displacement." On the basis of studies made on dummies in Nevada bomb tests, Clayton S. White estimated that "human missiles" would cause injuries to people over an area of up to 800 square miles. One is tempted to remark that man may become his worst enemy if "translated" by a nuclear blast.

The human body is remarkably rugged when it comes to withstanding the direct overpressure of the bomb blast. But this pressure could rupture eardrums over an area of 300 square miles and cause lung damage over 100 square miles. Inside a fragile building hit by the blast, people would be much more vulnerable. Many would be pinned down or buried by falling debris; some would be suffocated or burned to death. Rescue teams might be kept away from the collapsed and burning buildings by heavy fallout.

Radioactivity

Finally, we must consider the nuclear radiation emitted by the bomb and its radioactive products. We distinguish between the radiation emitted immediately and the delayed or residual radiation associated with fallout. The initial burst of nuclear radiation consists of neutrons and gamma rays; these can produce a lethal effect in people standing in the open 2.2 miles from Ground Zero. Since the fireball and blast would kill victims within this small area anyway, we need not spend much time discussing this particular danger. The main concern about the radiation hazard *per se* is the residual radiation or fallout.

Let us pick up the history of the atomic explosion which we left in mid-air with the fireball ascending into the sky. We mentioned that debris dislodged from the crater area is sucked up into the churning fireball. It is carried aloft by the turbulence inside the mass of flame and permeates the mushroom cloud at the top. In the process of being swept through the fireball, the inert debris is made highly radioactive, because the fission products attach themselves firmly to the debris particles. The fission-product atoms include more than 200 different radioactive species. Many of these are so short-lived (decaying within seconds or minutes) that they lose their radioactivity before the mushroom cloud has broken up. But a large proportion will have a lifetime of days, months, or many years.

The bomb cloud formed by a ten-megaton explosion will tower from 60,000 to 90,000 feet above the earth and stretch across many miles. As the high-altitude winds disperse the billowing cloud, the heavier particles of debris will fall back to earth (mostly within the first hour) and many of the lighter ones will be carried downwind. This "local" fallout will be spread in irregularly shaped patterns over an area of 100 to 500 miles, depending on the wind structure.

A bomb exploded at low altitude deposits about 80 per cent of its fallout locally or in a rather narrow zone around the world. The rest is injected into the stratosphere and is distributed globally. It is to be expected that in the case of bombs exploded in the middle latitudes of the Northern Hemisphere, half of the fission-product debris carried into the stratosphere would fall out within a year, chiefly in the heavily populated temperate latitudes of the same hemisphere.

Our concern here is mainly with local fallout, but let us consider for a moment how much effect a 10,000-megaton attack upon the United States would have on the rest of the world. Assuming that the fission-fusion-fission bombs derived 60 per cent of their explosive energy from fission, the fission products would amount to the equivalent of 6,000 megatons. Let us say that one fourth of this, or the equivalent of 1,500 megatons, goes into the stratosphere and is dispersed globally. This is about 25 times the total of fission products injected into the stratosphere by the weapons tests of the nuclear powers up to 1959. The annual dose of radiation in the Northern Hemisphere from those tests is estimated to be about 0.01 of a roentgen. If we multiply that by 25, we see that the stratospheric fallout from a 10,000-megaton attack would amount to about 0.25 of a roentgen, or several roentgens if we allow for geographical variations. This global consequence of a nuclear war (speaking only of the fallout effects) is insignificant in comparison with the other results of such a war.

The First Week

We return now to our discussion of the local fallout in the United States from the hypothetical 3,000-megaton attack we were considering. We assume that about 2,000 megatons of this explosive energy will be from fission, and perhaps three quarters of the fission products will fall out locally. That amount of radioactivity, corresponding to 1,500 megatons, could produce a level of contamination amounting to two kilotons per square mile over 750,000 square miles, or roughly one quarter of the United States land area.

How much radiation would this level of fallout produce? To calculate the radiation intensity we must invoke a timetable. Let us start with one hour after the explosion. On the basis of the method of calculation used in the official AEC report called "The Effects of Nuclear Weapons," we would arrive at the figure of 2,500 roentgens per hour as the intensity of the fallout an hour after the explosion. On the basis of more recent data from the Naval Radiological Defense Laboratory, the figure would be 7,500 roentgens. To be conservative, I have adopted a compromise estimate of 4,000 roentgens per hour as the first-hour level.

This value is meaningful only where the fallout actually descends to earth within the first hour; obviously it would not hold true for regions far downwind, where the fallout does not arrive for several hours. At that stage much of the short-lived radioactivity has decayed. Thus people far downwind are spared the great lethality that fallout possesses during its very early life.

We now need to know how the radioactivity drops off with the passage of time. It is usually assumed that the decay in activity follows a law known as the $t^{-1.2}$ rule: that is, the activity decreases tenfold for every sevenfold increase in time. Thus after seven hours the activity will be one tenth that at one hour; after 49 hours, it will be one hundredth, and so on. At the end of two weeks it will have dropped to one thousandth; after three months, to one 10,000th.

The $t^{-1.2}$ rule is a theoretical approximation, and in practice one has to resort to a more exact calculation and take account of a number of complicating factors. For example, the formula applies to radiation dosage at a point three feet above a flat, infinite plane which is uniformly contaminated. Any surface roughness will alter the result. Furthermore, some of the fission products are gases, and these do not fall out in proportion to their production. Finally, the various fission products have differing physical and chemical properties which affect their travels, their rate of fall, their adhesion to objects such as foliage, their incorporation in the soil, and so forth.

Reckoning in the complications by a rather lengthy and technical analysis, the writer has composed a timetable estimating the radiation dosage in the first 24 hours to a person standing in the open.

HOURS AFTER THE EXPLOSION	ROENTGEN DOSE
1 to 2	2,500
2 to 3	1,250
3 to 4	800
4 to 5	550
5 to 10	1,500
10 to 24	1,550

Each hour that fallout remains airborne reduces the human exposure by hundreds and even thousands of roentgens. Thus, if a person is far enough downwind so that the bomb debris is three hours old when it reaches him, he is spared 3,750 roentgens that he would have received between the first and third hours. By the end of five hours the fallout has lost enough activity so that people whose exposure begins at that point are spared 5,100 roentgens, and in the 24-hour period after the explosion they would receive 3,050 roentgens instead of 8,150. This is still a lethal dose.

It is possible to apply a yardstick to predict the acute or immediate effects from various doses of radiation received within a short time.

DOSE IN ROENTGENS	BIOLOGICAL EFFECT
0 to 100	No acute effects.
100 to 200	Radiation sickness; recovery in a few days.
200 to 300	Radiation sickness; for a few, death after several weeks.
300 to 400	Death for about one third of the exposed persons within several weeks.
400 to 600	Death for 35 to 90 per cent.
1000	No survivors; death within one week.
4000	Death within two days.

Radiation sickness is characterized by nausea, vomiting, and malaise during the first day. For roughly two weeks afterward, there may be no symptoms even in case of a lethal dose. Then ominous signs begin to appear, notably loss of hair. Other signs of acute radiation damage, which may come promptly or after a delay, include a rise in temperature, bloody diarrhea, bleeding from the gums, and extreme fatigue. A very high dose may produce convulsions and irrational behavior within the first day.

The major share of the dose from local fallout is delivered the first day. If radiation did not have a cumulative effect, the chances of survival would be excellent if one could limit his exposure the first day to 200 roentgens. But since he will be subject to continuing and cumulative fallout radiation, the first-day dose should not exceed 100 r.

If a person within the area where fallout begins at five hours is to keep his first-day dose below 100 r, he must have shelter that will reduce his exposure by a factor of at least 30 to 80 (in view of the dose range of 3,000 to 8,000 in the open). It would be better to have a protection factor of 100 to 500, but this would require specially built underground shelters; in view of the present state of our civil defenses and their probable state in the near future, one must be realistic and think in terms of shelter that exists today or can be improvised quickly.

The ordinary basement, such as is common in houses in the northern part of the United States, would provide a protection factor of only 10 to 20. This might be adequate for areas far downwind, but for millions of people caught in the vicinity of the burst it would not suffice. Additional protection could be gained at the last moment (even while the fallout was still airborne) by digging a short tunnel into the basement wall or by making an igloo in a corner of the basement with bags of sand, coal, or soil.

Below the Mason-Dixon Line many houses lack basements, but people might get sufficient protection by digging foxholes in the ground.

How would people know whether they had actually escaped a lethal dose? A survey of the fallout area with reliable radiation-measuring instruments could estimate the general level of contamination, but such a survey might not be made promptly and in any case would not necessarily indicate individual exposures. There are, however, simple and reliable radiation dosimeters, available commercially at low cost, which people could carry on their persons.

If a person has no assurance that his radiation dose is low, he may well panic when he sees people around him with obvious signs of radiation sickness. This argues against trying to cope with fallout by evacuating populations. Furthermore, the triple combination of the multimegaton bomb, the vast areas contaminable with fallout, and the random pattern of missile bombing makes evacuation a precarious policy. In too many cases the evacuees would be jumping from the frying pan into the fire. One should not attempt to play tag with fallout. The first rule of survival in nuclear war must be to seek immediate shelter, improvised if necessary.

We estimated that the first-day dose to a person exposed in the open for 24 hours would be some 8,000 roentgens. The second day the 24-hour dose would drop to 950 r (about twice the lethal dose); the third day, to 500 r; the fourth day, 300 r; the fifth day, 225 r; the sixth day, 175 r; and the seventh day, 120 r.

Considering the cumulative effect, it would be desirable to limit the second-day dose to ten r by means of shelter, and the doses on succeeding days to corresponding levels. Thus one would have to stay "buttoned up" for the first few days even though no food was available. By the third day, when the outside radiation level had dropped to ten r per hour, people beyond the reproductive age (*i.e.*, those not concerned about damage to the germ cells) could make quick dashes outside for emergency necessities. The radiation would still be too intense to permit relief parties to work in the area. However, if an adult beyond the reproductive phase of life were skilled in radiation lore and had instruments to measure his exposure, he might spend an hour or so attempting to decontaminate his house. He would accept a risk to himself in order to minimize the hazard to his family. The extent to which he could decontaminate his house would depend upon its construction: the size and shape of the roof, the nature of the roofing and siding. In favorable circumstances a determined householder might reduce the roof contamination tenfold by sweeping and scrubbing.

The Persisting Danger

By the end of the first week, when the radiation level outside dropped to four r per hour, the family could emerge from special shelters and live in the basement. There would still be considerable radiation there, not only from the roof (unless some fallout were washed off by scrubbing or heavy rain) but also from fission products contaminating the area around the house. If one stands upon a uniformly contaminated field, about half of the radiation dose comes from an area within 30 feet. It is very difficult to predict how fallout will be distributed in densely built-up areas, and one would expect very considerable variations in the intensity of fallout. A flat, tarred roof would tend to be much more contaminated than a steeply angled slate roof, for example.

The Naval Radiological Defense Laboratory at San Francisco has had considerable experience in decontaminating ships. Its experts claim that a tenfold reduction in contamination is not too difficult to attain, but going to a hundredfold decontamination is less feasible. Based upon actual experience in decontamination, it does appear that clean-up of contaminated areas will produce a significant benefit to survivors.

After the first week, the total dose for the next three weeks in a contaminated area would amount to 960 r. By clean-up operations, and by spending part of the time under shelter, the survivors might reduce their exposure for this period twenty-fold—that is, to 48 r. Such a dose would probably be acceptable for adults but would not be recommended for children. The reason for this dual standard is twofold. First, one wishes to protect those whose child-bearing years lie ahead in order to minimize the number of mutations introduced into the next generation. Secondly, young people are more likely to suffer the long-range bodily effects of radiation. Some of the delayed effects, such as cancer, will appear many years after irradiation and may be of little concern to older people.

After the first month, the fallout hazard in most areas would no longer be the overriding problem of life. The outdoors dose in the second month would still be about 220 r, but this could easily be reduced to ten or 20 r by cautious living—using shelter much of the time. At such a rate of exposure, a person who had already received 200 r in the first month would not be too worried about the radiation: he would be more concerned about regaining some creature comforts—adequate housing, better food, and so on. Here it is important to emphasize that the radiation dose a person will accept in a wartime risk situation is many times higher than that allowable in peacetime. The problem is one of sheer survival, and the risks must be judged accordingly.

By the third month the radiation dose from the environment would fall to less than 100 r, and a return to near-normal living would become possible for almost all communities in the local-fallout areas. Of course caution would be necessary, but the acute phase would have passed. The principal activity (no pun intended) would be recovery of the community as a functioning entity. It might well be that the mortality, the damage, and the disruption of the national economy would be so great that each community would be forced to look to its own needs and supply them from its own region. This implies a kind of colonial existence in which manpower would concentrate on one essential—food.

It may come as something of a surprise to be told that the acute radiation hazard would vanish within a few months after a 3,000-megaton attack. There has been much in print about areas being denied to human habitation for years. This misconception is due in part to a failure to realize that the attitude toward risks would change in wartime, but even more to an actual overestimate of the long-term radiation hazard. It used to be thought that in the second half-year after such an attack the radiation dose from fallout would be some 500 r, but on the basis of recent evidence I would estimate that it would be only 60 r. Strict adherence to the $t^{-1.2}$ law made it appear that people would have to live in shelters for years, whereas the present changed picture of the persisting hazard greatly modifies the shelter problem.

After three years the principal gamma emitter in fallout is the long-lived isotope cesium 137. However, only part of it appears in the heavy local fallout, because when created in the fireball it is in gaseous form. This is fortunate, for cesium's chemical properties tend to fix it in the upper inch of the soil surface, where it can readily emit its radiation to the surroundings. The best way to deal with cesium 137 that falls on the soil is to plow it under.

In a nuclear war, the external, or gamma, radiation would be the prime hazard of fallout. But the hazard of internal radiation from ingested fission products would also be serious during the acute phase. Interest here concentrates on the lodging of radio-iodine in the thyroid, gross fission products in the gastro-intestinal tract and bone-seekers such as radiostrontium. Probably the internal hazard would be much less than the external, but gas masks might be desirable for a time, and the population would have to be careful to avoid contaminated food and water.

Strontium 90

Finally, there is the longer-term problem of food grown on the contaminated soil. Fallout corresponding to two kilotons per square mile would mean a burden of 200 curies of strontium 90 per square mile. No one is sure just how much of this activity would be deposited in the soil. But of course the contamination of the soil would be of a much higher order of magnitude than the levels from test fallout that have been considered in the preceding chapters of this book. Food grown on soil contaminated to the level of two kilotons per square mile could ultimately give people a body burden of about 30,000 strontium units—incomparably greater than the 67 strontium units now recommended by the International Commission on Radiological Protection as the maximum permissible concentration for the general population. But in a nuclear war peacetime standards would be forgotten. What, then, would be a reasonable wartime limit—for children, for adults, and under various circumstances? The author does not propose to make any recommendations on this score. It would require a rather sophisticated analysis to determine the strontium 90 content of foods and set up standards, and it would be impossible to apply such a system in the wake of war. The survivors would be wise to subsist on foods stored before the attack or on edibles not exposed to heavy fallout, rather than run the risks of the acute strontium 90 hazard from severely contaminated lands.

Besides the fission products there would be other radioactive materials formed from the bomb elements or induced in the environment by neutrons. It is difficult to estimate the amount of these induced activities; all one can say is that they would add to the radiation hazard but would not generally be as serious as the fission products.

Saturation Attacks

The nuclear radiation hazard has been emphasized because of its unique characteristics, its great lethality, its spread over a wide area, its persistence in time, and its many-sided attack upon the living organism. Nuclear radiation is potentially the greatest killer of all the weapon effects, and certainly one of the most difficult hazards to combat. It is a very effective weapon even though it represents only 10 per cent of the bomb's energy.

Fallout presents the possibility of a veritable "saturation" attack, meaning that it could envelop an entire nation in lethality. This may seem incredible in view of the very large land masses of the United States and the U.S.S.R. However, analytic appraisals by defense experts show that in a nation such as the United States an attack with 10,000 megatons of high-yield fission weapons would kill approximately 80 per cent of the population (if unsheltered) within 60 days. A 20,000-megaton attack would kill 95 per cent; in other words, it would virtually saturate the nation with lethal fallout. Because of its larger land area the U.S.S.R. would not saturate quite as quickly, but a 10,000-megaton attack would mean about 75 per cent mortality, and a 20,000-megaton attack would raise this figure to roughly 90 per cent.

It would be pleasant to suppose that such high levels of attack are purely hypothetical and have no relation to the actual potential of the world's stockpiled weapons. Such, however, is not the case. Present stockpiles are more than adequate to spread radioactive lethality over an entire continental land mass. This is part of the new dimension of nuclear warfare.

12 JOHN M. FOWLER

National Survival

The portrait of the superbomb is now complete. We have examined its destructive potential and have followed in detail the radioactive dust that finds its way into the soil, into man's food, and into the body. Within the body we have seen the mischief that can be caused by the radiation released. We have assessed the fallout risks to individuals and have learned of the special hazard posed to the reproductive cells in which man stores his future.

With the help of the analyses of biological damage in Chapters 5 and 6, we can compute what the peacetime testing of nuclear weapons, even with all the precautions taken, has cost us in lives lost or made less useful.

Walter Guild estimates that for each strontium unit in the bones there will be two to six cases of leukemia per year per 100 million of population. Thus if the average level is ten strontium units over the next 30 years, as our calculations indicate, there may be 1,200 to 3,600 cases of leukemia in the United States and perhaps 20,000 in the world during this generation.

The genetic damage is of about the same order of magnitude. James Crow has given us an estimate that the number of genetic defects in the children of the present generation may amount to 20,000 or possibly even several times that. And the genetic harm will persist in the generations to come.

When we add the man-days lost through life-shortening and the misery and death caused by bone cancer, we have an impressive absolute number of people hurt by the current fallout. In relative terms, however, the risk is much less impressive. Military preparedness inevitably costs lives: there are some 1,400 deaths each year in our armed forces from peacetime accidents. It is easy to see why persons with responsibility for our military strength are irritated at the—to them—petty quibbling over the biological cost of nuclear weapon testing. Yet to those who believe that reliance on nuclear deterrence will lead us closer to war, the waste of life, especially of lives in countries not engaged in the power struggle, presents a moral burden too great to assume. Thus their deploring of bomb-testing and their "nit-picking" over strontium 90 levels in milk are secondary to their real concern: that this H-bomb, which distresses us even in peacetime, may be our final undoing in war.

It is clear to everyone that the hydrogen bomb is not just an improved bow and arrow, not just a more powerful and compact weapon, to be reduced to a training manual and a procedure for assembly and disassembly. In the preceding chapter Ralph Lapp briefly pulled aside the curtain and let us look at its potential use. His summary of the possibilities of personal survival in a nuclear war is a sobering one. A skilled and resourceful individual or family outside the ring of complete destruction and on the outskirts of the lethal umbrella of fallout might survive the nightmarish early weeks. By burrowing into the walls of the basement or huddling under some hastily improvised shield in a corner, a person might survive although the outdoors was an oven of silent death.

A Country Laid Waste

Survival through those early weeks would be a personal job; one could expect little organized community help. Let us now try to imagine what kind of country and world a surviving family would crawl back into when their pocket dosimeter told them that the outside radiation levels no longer threatened immediate death. The "nuclear war hearings" of the Special Subcommittee on Radiation of the Joint Committee on Atomic Energy in 1959 attempted to provide, at least in outline, such a picture. Defense Department experts, aided by government scientists from the AEC and various research laboratories, examined the hypothetical results of an attack on the United States which would release 1,490 megatons of fission energy. (For some of the detailed information presented at the hearings, see Appendix D.)

To illustrate the part played by weather conditions, the experts chose October 17, 1958, as the day of the attack. A meteorological map showed how the fallout from the bombs would be distributed across the country (see Figure 21). The heaviest fallout fell upon the area east of the Mississippi River. The East Coast was devastated. In the New York metropolitan area 65 per cent of the population was killed or injured, in Boston 91 per cent, in Philadelphia 80 per cent, in Baltimore 92 per cent, in Washington 81 per cent.

Such an attack would destroy much of the nation's economic, governmental, and cultural structure. The cities' casualties would include an inordinately large proportion of the nation's executive personnel and technical experts. For instance, 80 per cent of all our aeronautical engineers live in 17 metropolitan areas; about 90 per cent of the top officers of the 180 largest American corporations are concentrated in fewer than 40 cities and their suburbs. The big-city concentration of our doctors, research scientists, lawyers, artists, musicians, etc., is equally high.

For the first few days after the attack every target city would be totally disorganized. The injured would lack medical care, because of the destruction of hospitals, the scarcity of doctors, and the lethal fallout in the streets barring all movement or entry from outside the city. The surviving populace, stunned by the terrible blow and seeing those around them suffering from acute radiation symptoms, would be thrown into panic.

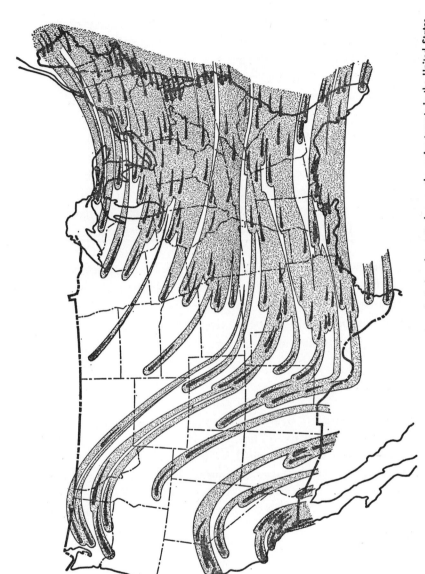

FIG. 21. Pattern of fallout on the second day after a hypothetical nuclear attack upon the major targets in the United States on October 17, 1958. The meteorological conditions (wind, rain, etc.) on that day would have produced the fallout distribution shown on this map.

The depletion of white blood cells in the irradiated victims would open the way to infection and pestilence. Without organized rescue or medical facilities, even seemingly minor infections would take a fatal toll.

It seems clear from testimony at the hearings that the attack envisaged would completely destroy urban life as we know it. The few survivors, as soon as they could venture out, would leave their blasted cities and trek into the countryside. The cities' complex technological life would cease. Even undamaged factories would be unable to function, because of a complete breakdown of transportation and inability to get raw material. Life in the United States would largely regress to a rural economy.

The countryside would certainly not be left undamaged. A compelling description of some of the ecological effects of a nuclear attack was given at the hearings by John N. Wolfe, chief of environmental sciences in the AEC's Division of Biology and Medicine. His statement in part:

> Fire . . . in the dry season of mid-October would spread over enormous areas of dry western coniferous forests and grasslands, with concomitant destruction of natural living resources and their habitats. It is most likely, in my opinion, that these fires would go unchecked until quenched by the winter snows, spreading over hundreds of thousands of square miles. In the eastern United States, the dry oak and pine forests of the Blue Ridge and Appalachians from New England to Virginia, adjacent to multiple detonations, would undergo a like fate, as well as the pine on the southern Atlantic and Gulf Coastal Plains. In the agricultural land of the Mississippi Valley, with the crops harvested, fire is likely to be more local, less severe, but widespread. Add to this the denuding effects of radiation and/or chemically toxic materials.
>
> With the coming of spring thaws, especially in the mountains, meltwater from the mountain glaciers and snowfields would erode the denuded slopes, flood the valleys, in time rendering them uninhabitable and unexploitable for decades or longer. Re-

moval of the turf by fire and erosion on plains and prairie would result in uncheckable erosion by wind, with subsequent expansion of present "dust bowls" and creation of new ones of wide extent. Emergency overgrazing and cultivation (if there were those to work) would wreak further havoc. . . .

Along with fire, flood and erosion . . . would come intensification of disease—plant and animal, including man. Moreover, in the less irradiated areas, populations of deleterious animals, especially insects, would move in—a further detriment to food production and contributing further to its unavailability to surviving people.

Man's access to succor through hospitalization, treatment, communications, etc., would be meager, and thus the inroads of starvation would be accentuated by increased incidence and intensity of disease.

The immediate physical effects (other than radiation) could be particularly catastrophic in such areas as the Los Angeles watershed, where the city is almost surrounded by vegetation susceptible to the inroads of fire. Those islands relatively free of radioactivity in the early stages would be increasingly contaminated by redistribution of radioactive materials by wind, water, biotic migration, and precipitation. . . . Animals able to move into the "clean" areas will be contaminated survivors from adjacent areas, and probably both the wild and the domesticated animals will be unfit for human food.

I visualize those people unsheltered in heavy fallout areas after three months to be dead, dying, sick, or helpless; those sheltered, if they can psychologically withstand confinement for that period, will emerge to a strange landscape. The sun will shine through a dust-laden atmosphere; the landscape in mid-January would be snow-covered or blackened by fire; at higher latitudes blizzards and sub-zero temperatures would add death and discomfort; both food and shelter would be inadequate and production incapacitated. Come then spring floods, and soon after, adding measurably to the disrupted pattern of human existence, [will come storms] such as hurricanes and tornadoes, for which there is no defense, and after which there will be little aid. . . .

The long-term ecological effects of nuclear war are difficult to assess. However, with the advent of that first spring, I would assume the beginnings of a gradual return to equilibrium of the biological environment. I would anticipate that in springs and summers in the decades that follow, biotic succession would continue, leading to full ecological recovery.

The role of North American man in this long-term view of environment—his nationality, genetic constitution, psychological make-up, and creative potential three, ten, or 100 generations later—I leave for others to predict.

The Aftermath

Our confidence in man's will to live causes us to share the feeling that the country would rebuild. It would be a tortuous job, much complicated by the tremendous burden of radioactivity on the cities and countryside. Three to five years after the attack the strontium 90 level would average about 1,000 millicuries per square mile in the most lightly hit sections, and as high as 300,000 millicuries in some areas. In other words, the burden would be from ten to 3,000 times as great as the maximum of 100 millicuries per square mile from the bomb tests, which we estimated will load a person's skeleton with 7.6 strontium units for 70 years. If we use Professor Guild's figure of two to six leukemias per 100 million per strontium unit per year, we can see that the incidence of leukemia after a nuclear attack would be staggering.

The strontium 90 fallout would be heavy all around the world (see Figure 22). The average in the North Temperate Zone would be about 1,000 millicuries per square mile. Since 80 per cent of the world's population lives in this region, Professor Guild's figures would give an estimate of from 3,600 to 11,000 leukemias per year if this strontium in the soil got into the diet in the same ratio as that from testing has. Moreover, local concentrations would raise the leukemia total much higher. On the densely populated United States East Coast, for instance, the strontium 90 levels would be 100 times the world average. No food could safely be grown in this soil. Even in

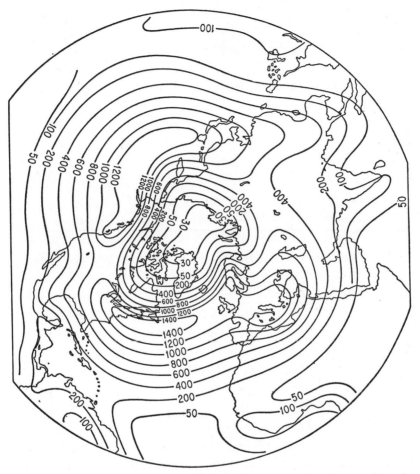

FIG. 22. World-wide strontium 90 fallout after a hypothetical nuclear attack on the United States. These figures represent the radioactive contamination of the soil (in millicuries per square mile) three to five years after the attack.

the midwest much of the farm land would be too contaminated to use for a generation.

As for genetic damage, much of the country's population would be exposed to levels of from 100 to 1,000 roentgens over a lifetime. James V. Neel, a geneticist who has studied the Hiroshima and Nagasaki populace in some detail, estimated at the hearings that, assuming 40 million persons survived the attack, in the next 30 generations there might be anywhere between 4.8

million and 384 million deaths among children at or before
birth, between 240,000 and 38 million persons born with obvious
defects, and between 12 million and 768 million persons with
impaired vigor or fertility. (The wide ranges in these figures
reflect the many uncertainties in the assumptions behind the
estimates.)

Carbon 14 would be produced in enormous amount in a
nuclear war: the level might be 20 times higher than the present
natural level for a few decades. Because of its very long half-
life, over the long run radiocarbon would add a costly genetic
toll to that of the other radiations.

No less appalling is the general life-shortening effect of the
fallout. Testimony about the cost of the hypothetical nuclear
war in these terms was given at the hearings by Hardin B. Jones,
professor of medical physics and physiology at the Donner
Laboratory in California. If the average radiation dose was 300 r
the first week after the attack and 100 r more in the first year,
the average United States resident would have his life shortened by about 11 years. This cost is perhaps the greatest of all
the long-range effects—about two billion man-years wasted in
this country alone.

In spite of such facts, a flavor of optimism seemed to pervade
the Congressional hearings and newspaper reports of them. For
example, the St. Louis *Post-Dispatch* of August 13, 1959, published a UPI dispatch from Washington under the headline,
DENIES NUCLEAR WAR WOULD WIPE OUT CIVILI-
ZATION:

> Expert witnesses at the hearing described the horrors of
> nuclear war, but they also disputed several popular notions. They
> asserted, for example that:
> The hydrogen bomb cannot wipe out mankind.
> It cannot destroy civilization and the world's economy.
> People can be protected in large measure against the bomb's
>   radiations and fire and, to some extent, against its blast.
> With such protection, the nation could survive a nuclear war
>   and make a comeback.

A look at the casualty statistics and a knowledge of the destructive power of the bombs gives one the feeling that if a
nuclear war could not destroy civilization and the economy in
the warring countries, then perhaps we do not understand what
is meant by civilization and national economy. Certainly a
nation's language and many technological and cultural ideas
would survive with the human survivors; but much of the
material basis of civilization, the knowledge stored in libraries,
and the human talent would be gone.

The meteorological effects discussed by Dr. Machta in Chapter 2 would tend to spare the Southern Hemisphere, and the
center of power would probably shift south, where there are
populations with huge capabilities for growth. Fred Charles
Iklé, whose *The Social Impact of Bomb Destruction* presents a
useful and sobering picture of the effects of a nuclear disaster
on people and their social institutions, has considered the after-
math of such a war. He says:

> Those speculatively inclined, then, ought to picture the world,
> after an all-out nuclear war with extreme fallout contamination,
> not as a planet inhabited only by lower forms of plant life im-
> mune to radioactivity, but as a world with expanding popula-
> tions and perhaps thriving economies in South America, South
> Africa, Indonesia, Australia, and New Zealand. From this pic-
> ture one might try to look still farther ahead and perhaps reach
> the conclusion that the surviving generations would be farther
> away from a peaceful millennium than ever, because of the deep
> racial, religious, and ideological differences that divide the
> peoples of the Southern Hemisphere. Indeed—thus this specula-
> tion could continue—both capitalism and communism might sur-
> vive, since both might be represented among the survivor
> nations. But the powerful states which fought for these issues
> would have disappeared from history—much as the Inca Empire
> and the realm of Carthage have ended forever.

The nuclear war hearings, in giving flesh and substance to
the nightmare of such a war, did not make it appear more

tolerable. The powerful nations of the world are still confronted with their policy dilemma: war, the traditional recourse when diplomacy fails or unslakable ambitions clash, is now denied them. There have been many suggestions of ways to escape this dilemma, and most of them are aimed at making war possible by limiting it.

Many strategists insist that limited wars with "tactical" nuclear weapons are feasible and even necessary. In *Our Nuclear Future* Edward Teller makes the nuclear warfare of the future sound like a modern sequel to King Arthur's Court—Sir Lancelots armed with "clean" nuclear weapons fighting it out on the plains and oceans away from the cities. But the terrible weapons may not always be in the hands of rational men. It seems to many of us that the concept of a limited or limitable war is a dangerous idea which may lead us down a one-way street to an H-bomb war.

This view is shared by as eminent a military expert as General Lauris Norstad, the NATO commander. Asked by Congressman Gary of Virginia, "Could you not have a limited war and still use atomic weapons?" General Norstad replied:

> I do not agree with those people who say you can control the size of this fire, the size of this blast, neatly, cold-bloodedly, once it starts. I think it is the most dangerous and disastrous thing in the world. I think you must prevent the thing from starting in the first place, because once it starts in a critical area such as the NATO area, it is more likely than not, in my opinion, to explode into the whole thing, whether we like it or the Russians like it or anybody likes it.

"Clean" bombs have been put forth as a way to make war possible by sparing civilian populations. No doubt experimentation could produce bombs with a greatly reduced fallout. Although such bombs would turn the urban centers of the world into vast crematoria, they would avoid contaminating whole nations or continents. But when the chips are down, will clean bombs be used? When our radar picket lines and our "Operation Teepee" surveillance tell us that the missiles are on the way, who will tell us whether they are clean? In such a one-shot war will not the need for the greatest "bang for a buck" overcome any squeamishness over radioactivity? The very dirty fission-fusion-fission bombs are most economical to deliver in terms of destruction per ton of payload. The fusion core needs a tamper to hold it together while it is being heated by the A-bomb trigger. Uranium 238 serves as an excellent tamper: denser than lead, it provides the massiveness needed to hold the bomb together those vital few microseconds, and, far from being dead weight, it becomes a part of the fissionable explosive. How can one hope for wars in which such an ideal weapon will not be used?

Congressman Holifield in Chapter 9 urges an intelligently directed civil-defense program as a means of assuring our nation's survival from a nuclear attack. Ralph Lapp's chapter on personal survival also speaks strongly for such measures. I must confess that after reading it I was strongly prompted to order a pocket dosimeter and lay in stores of reserve food. Even the idea of attacking the basement wall with a pick did not seem unreasonable.

If a nuclear attack comes, there can be no question that we will all wish for shelters, dosimeters, and unradioactive food. But will that be enough? When we emerge from our shelters, be they G.I. or do-it-yourself basement tunnels, what sort of world shall we have? And what are the chances of our being prepared with adequate shelters? A shelter program would be costly: estimates at the hearings were from five to 20 billions of dollars. Although it is true that shelters would have some influence in deterring an attack, to most people it will seem foolish to spend billions of dollars to bury the nation underground when it so desperately needs schools and teachers, highways, adequate health programs, etc. To a half-starved world it would be another example of our self-centered approach to world problems. I would prefer to see the time, energy, and money spent on purposes more productive than civil defense.

A More Solid Basis

We must find an alternative to war rather than try to make it possible again. To many of us, a world armed with nuclear weapons and continually in a posture of deterrence is an intolerably unstable world. More and more, disarmament is being put forward by "practical" men as the only possible way out. In a brilliant essay called "Man and the Atom" in the *Bulletin of the Atomic Scientists*, Max Born, the German physicist and Nobel laureate, summed up this viewpoint:

> There is no doubt that the human race is in an acute crisis. At the present time, fear alone enforces a precarious peace. However, that is an unstable state of affairs, which ought to be replaced by something better.
>
> We do not need to look far in order to find a more solid basis for the proper conduct of our affairs: It is the principle which is common to all great religions and with which all moral philosophers agree; the principle which in our own part of the world is taught by the doctrine of Christianity; the principle which Mahatma Gandhi had actually carried into practice, before our own eyes, in liberating his own country, India, from foreign domination: It is the renunciation of force in the pursuit of political aims.
>
> Fifty years ago, when I was young, this statement would have been regarded as Utopian and foolish. Today I am able to express it without raising doubts as to my sanity. It is very likely that tomorrow not the pacifists but the bellicose will be regarded as fools, for the experiences of the last 50 years have left an impact on the minds of men. Yet I feel unequal to the task of analyzing and discussing this immense problem in all its aspects. What would I be able to add to the words of the great poets and prophets of our time? I have in mind the address given by Albert Schweitzer when he received the Nobel Peace Prize; the declaration published by Albert Einstein, a short time before his death, together with Bertrand Russell and other scholars of many nations; the Mainau manifesto signed by 52 Nobel laure-

ates; and many other similar declarations. Today these voices no longer die away unheard, for the man in the street—and perhaps also some of the great of this world—listen to them.

Sentiments of this nature have long existed among scientists, perhaps because they were the first to sense the terrible shadow that the mushroom cloud had cast over mankind's future. Individually and through their political voice, the Federation of American Scientists, they have in great numbers called for a more vigorous and more positive approach to disarmament. They decry the dangerous imbalance of a policy which spends 40 billions of dollars for armaments and not a hundredth of that for disarmament studies, of a government which lavishly backs weapons research but puts nothing into research for peace, of a Congress which allows 2.4 million dollars to the Department of Defense for legislative liaison" (which sounds suspiciously like public relations) but rejects Senator Humphrey's attempt to provide half a million dollars for technical and scientific studies of armament control.

Surely this single-minded allocation of billions to wars, hot and cold, must cease, and "peace spending" must become as acceptable a reason for taxes as defense spending. With money and government backing, some of the research talent of this richly endowed country, instead of developing nuclear weapons and the missiles to carry them, could be directed to search for ways to eliminate the necessity for them.

Man has opened the nucleus and probed its secrets; there is no turning back on that. We now see clearly the two faces of the nuclear future. If we place our reliance on the H-bomb and on the even more devastating nuclear weapons that will surely come, we must watch the radioactivity in our environment slowly rise and must be prepared to pay a price in terms of death, disease, and mutation. We shall always be under the terrible threat of a civilization-crippling nuclear war. If, instead, we concentrate energy and money toward a solution to war, the path will still be difficult and precarious. We may fail. We may not be able to preserve everything that we want in our political, cultural, and economic ways of life. So there are risks in either course. But as Bertrand Russell has said, ". . . If risks must be run, is it not better to run the risks in pursuit of something ennobling and splendid rather than in the perfecting of weapons of man's destruction?"

The choice must be made and must be made now. The resumption of testing, the building of hardened missile bases in the food-producing areas of the United States, the equipping of our allies with nuclear weapons—all these imminent questions are a part of the decision. The voice that finally decides should not be that of the scientist, the weapons expert, or the military tactician. It must belong to the great voting mass of the American people.

The road to disarmament is certainly not easy. We may lose our way along that twisting and dangerous path. But if we can banish the blight of war from the earth, then perhaps man can at last come out of the cave in which he has so long dwelt and walk upright in a land where the tamed nucleus powers his machines and the oceans are his fuel.

APPENDICES

Fundamentals of Radiation

Radiation has always been of extreme importance to mankind, but only in the last few decades have we begun to realize its variety and the subtle hazards associated with it. The word "radiation" itself is so broad and inclusive that we have to specify what kind we mean in particular instances. We use it generally to mean a transport of energy which does not depend upon any material carrier. Our most common example of radiation is the energy we receive from the sun; the successful transport of this energy through hundreds of thousands of miles of space illustrates radiation's independence of a carrying medium.

All radiation can be described in terms of particles, moving with tremendous velocities. The mechanism of energy transport then becomes rather clear: the particles have an energy of motion which they can give up on impact, much in the same way that a moving billiard ball can give all or part of its energy to another billiard ball with which it collides.

The particles involved in the discussion of fallout and its effects are listed in the table below. From the fact that mass 1 is only 1.67×10^{-24} of a gram, one may get some idea of the smallness of these particles.

PARTICLE	MASS	CHARGE	RANGE IN WATER AT 1 MEV
			(in inches)
photon	0	0	8
electron	1/1840	−1	.04
proton	1	+1	.0004
neutron	1	0	36+
alpha particle	4	+2	.00008

Photons

The photon is the particle that carries the energy of electro-magnetic radiation, including (besides light) radio, X-rays, etc. The penetrating power of the photon depends on its energy. The energy of a photon is a unique function of the kind of radiation, that is, of the wavelength. The most energetic photons are those of gamma rays, followed by X-rays, ultraviolet light, and visible light. The one characteristic all photons have in common is their speed: 3×10^{10} (*i.e.*, 30 billion) centimeters per second, or 186,000 miles per second. This speed is one of the fundamental constants of nature.

Electrons

The electron is the basic unit of negative charge and is a major component of all matter. It is so small that its dimensions have so far defied measurement. Its "weight" is correspondingly minute: 9.11×10^{-28} of a gram, or 3.22×10^{-30} of an ounce (*i.e.*, about three millionths of a trillionth of an ounce). Obviously so light a particle can easily be accelerated to very high velocities: the electrons with which we are concerned in radio-activity usually move with a velocity very nearly that of photons. Electrons emitted by a radioactive nucleus are called beta particles, and their emission is called beta-decay. Sometimes a nucleus emits a positive electron, or positron, which has the same mass as an electron and an equal but opposite charge. These two particles have about the same effect on biological systems.

Protons and Neutrons

The neutron and the proton, called "nucleons" because they are the building blocks of the nucleus, also are important as particles in bomb radiation. They are very much alike (their difference in mass is only 0.09 per cent) but whereas the proton has a positive charge (equal to the negative charge of the electron), the neutron is uncharged.

The *chemical* properties of an atom depend on the number of electrons it has and on their arrangement. Thus all atoms with the same number of electrons orbiting around the nucleus, and hence the same number of protons in the nucleus, are chemically equivalent, can form the same molecules, take part in the same processes, etc. Elements differ from one another in the number of electrons, but where the shell arrangement of the electrons is similar, different elements tend to have chemical properties in common. For example, calcium and strontium share a certain electron arrangement and consequently have similar chemical properties; potassium and cesium likewise are a pair of chemical brothers.

In 1932 Harold Urey discovered a kind of hydrogen which had the same nuclear charge as ordinary hydrogen but a different nuclear weight. Common hydrogen is a very simple atom: it consists of a proton with a single electron circling around it. The "heavy hydrogen" that Urey discovered has a neutron as well as a proton in its nucleus. This nucleus is called a deuteron, and the atom is called deuterium. Ordinary hydrogen and deuterium, having the same number of electrons but a different number of nucleons, are "isotopes." We call the first hydrogen 1 (because it has one nucleon) and the second hydrogen 2 (two nucleons—a proton and a neutron). The isotopes of an element have identical chemical properties but dissimilar nuclear properties. These are of critical importance in nuclear reactions.

Alpha Particles

The alpha particle is the nucleus of a helium atom, consisting of two protons and two neutrons. It is emitted in the decay of heavy nuclei, for example, radium. The alpha is the most massive and has the greatest charge of the radiation particles.

Nuclear Radioactivity

In radioactivity, the emissions we are concerned about are beta particles, alpha particles, and gamma rays. There are, in nature, several unstable elements that decay spontaneously: most of them are heavy elements which tend to emit alpha particles. Among these are uranium, radium, thorium, and polonium. Usually the nucleus left after the emission of the alpha particle is also radioactive. Radioactive isotopes of practically all the elements have now been produced artificially. This is usually done by adding or subtracting protons or neutrons. For example, if we substitute a neutron for one of the protons in ordinary nitrogen, nitrogen 14, it becomes carbon 14, a radioactive isotope of normal carbon 12. Eventually, carbon 14 spontaneously emits an electron and becomes nitrogen 14 again. It is of interest, of course, to know how long this process takes. For any given nucleus, prediction of the time of decay is impossible, but if we observe a large group, we see a certain statistical rate of emission, which is translated into the "half-life" of the isotope. The half-life of a radioactive species is perhaps its most characteristic feature and cannot be changed by external manipulations of any kind. It is the time during which half of the original nuclei will have emitted their radiation, or "decayed." If we started out with a dollar's worth of radioactive material X, one half-life later only fifty cents' worth would remain; another half-life later, a quarter's worth, and so on.

The product of a radioactive decay is called the daughter nucleus. The most important mother-daughter pairs that occur in fallout are strontium 90 and its daughter yttrium 90, and cesium 137 and barium 137.

A radioactive decay may yield more than one kind of emission. For instance, after a nucleus has emitted an alpha or a beta particle, the daughter nucleus may be left with an excess of energy (*i.e.*, in an "excited state"); it then emits a gamma ray which carries off this excess energy.

Alpha or beta particles are emitted because the configuration of particles in the nucleus is not a stable one. With its interesting regard for symmetry, nature tends to endow stable nuclei with an equal number of protons and neutrons. When either of these particles outnumbers the other, the nucleus tends to be unstable and to restore the balance by emitting an appropriate beta particle. A neutron-rich nucleus emits a negative electron, thus changing a neutron into a proton; a proton-rich nucleus emits a positive electron, changing a proton into a neutron. Carbon 14 has six protons and eight neutrons in its nucleus, and so it emits an electron, changes a neutron to a proton, and winds up with seven protons and seven neutrons—the stable nucleus nitrogen 14.

Alpha particles are emitted not from symmetry considerations but because the heavy elements have a strong tendency to break up into smaller, more tightly-bound pieces (the alpha particle is very tightly bound). Since the heavy elements have a surplus of neutrons, the loss of two protons and two neutrons leaves the relative proportion of protons and neutrons more unbalanced than before, so the daughter nucleus is more unstable and usually emits one or more beta particles, plus, in many cases, gamma rays.

The naturally occurring radioisotopes in our environment

consist mostly of heavy elements, which emit alpha particles and gamma rays; there is one lighter radioisotope of consequence, potassium 40, which emits beta particles.

The artificial radioisotopes that fallout has now added to our environment are a number of species of fission products (see Appendix B).

Cosmic Rays

The cosmic "rays" consist of protons, alpha particles, and heavier nuclei, accelerated to tremendous velocities in the vastness of intergalactic space. When they crash into the atoms of the earth's atmosphere, they demolish these nuclei and release showers of protons, neutrons, electrons, photons, and stranger particles. Because air absorbs the energy of the cosmic rays, we find that the intensity of this radiation increases as we rise to thinner air: the intensity roughly doubles each 5,000 feet from sea level up to 20,000 feet.

X-rays

X-rays are produced by a transformation of the energy of high-speed electrons when they are stopped by a target. The electrons are commonly accelerated to their high velocities by the application of a high voltage between their source, the "cathode," and the target, the "anode." This is the origin of the unit of energy used in radiation physics—the electron volt: it is the energy acquired by an electron going (in a vacuum) from the negative to the positive terminal of a one-volt battery. One electron volt is so tiny a quantity of energy that it is hard to grasp in common terms—it amounts to only 5×10^{-26} of a kilowatt hour! The usual X-ray machine has a voltage of a few hundred thousand volts, and the X-rays are measured in thousands of electron volts (kev). Research accelerators in particle physics speed up particles to millions of electron volts (Mev) and have entered the range of billions of electron volts (Bev). Cosmic rays are measured in thousands of Bevs.

Since the discovery of X-rays in 1896, their use in diagnosis has spread to all civilized countries. Because the penetrating power of X-rays can be regulated to some extent, they can be used to destroy tumors or other unwanted tissue. To minimize the exposure in making X-ray pictures, clinical radiologists and dentists use especially sensitive X-ray film. For exploratory diagnostic work (for instance, to locate a metal object swallowed by a child), the fluoroscope is used. A fluorescent screen replaces the X-ray film, so that the "picture," or shadows, can be seen directly. Because it takes more energy to excite this fluorescence than to make an image on a photographic plate, exposures in fluoroscopy are usually larger than in ordinary X-ray examination. The so-called "mini-films" used in the TB X-ray trailers involve photographing a fluorescent screen with an ordinary camera; because the camera lens is not as efficient as the human eye, this requires even larger exposures. The per capita exposure to X-rays during a lifetime is substantial, and surveys show that 75 to 90 per cent of this dose comes from diagnostic examinations.

An increasing source of radiation exposure is the medical use of radioactive elements. Some of these can be deposited selectively in certain areas of the body (for instance, radioactive iodine in the thyroid); some are used as tracers to give information about bodily functions.

Ionization

When a rapidly-moving charged particle passes through matter (*e.g.*, living tissue), it dislodges electrons from atoms in its path, because of the electrical attraction or repulsion between the particle and the electrons. It takes only ten to 100 electron volts of energy to tear an electron from an atom, and since a radiation particle usually has an energy of millions of electron volts, it can ionize many thousands of atoms before it is stopped.

An uncharged particle, such as the photon or the neutron, also can produce ionization, for when it collides with another particle, such as an electron or neutron, it gives up much of its energy to the latter, and the recoiling second particle ionizes the atoms it encounters.

Measures of Radiation

There are two common measures of radiation—physical and biological. The physical measurement is usually expressed in terms of the number of particles per second emitted by the source. The conventional unit, named after the French husband-and-wife team who contributed so much to the understanding of radioactivity, is the curie: the number of disintegrations per second in a gram of radium (37 billion). For fallout the convenient units are the millicurie (one thousandth of a curie), the microcurie (one millionth of a curie), and the micromicrocurie (one millionth of a millionth of a curie).

The biological measure, or dose, is based on the amount of energy absorbed by tissue, this absorption being a measure of the ionization produced and therefore of the damage that will be done to cells. One unit employed is the "rad," which is the absorption of 100 ergs by one gram of tissue. This unit is about the same as the "roentgen," which applies specifically to X-rays. Because the various nuclear radiations differ in biological effectiveness, the rad is translated into a general unit called the "rem": a dose of one rem of a given radiation is calculated as one rad times the RBE (relative biological efficiency) of that radiation. One millirem is a thousandth of a rem. The actual amounts of energy involved are extremely small. For instance, absorption of 500 rads would raise the temperature of a gram of tissue less than two thousandths of a degree Fahrenheit. Yet a 500-rad dose to the body is lethal.

To evaluate the hazards of fallout, we must consider the amount of radiation we are already receiving from other sources —natural and medical. This falls into two classes: external (*e.g.,* cosmic rays and X-rays) and internal (*e.g.,* radiopotassium and radiocarbon in the body). The accompanying table, from a United Nations study, gives the average dosage per year from ordinary sources to certain vulnerable organs.

	ANNUAL DOSE *(in millirem)*	
	To the Gonads	To the Bone Marrow
External		
Cosmic Rays	28	28
Terrestrial Radiation (in normal regions)	47	47
Atmospheric Radiation	2	2
Medical X-rays	20 to 150	up to 100 or more
Internal		
Potassium 40	19	11
Carbon 14	1.6	1.6
Radon-Thoron	2	2
Radium	0	0.5
Approximate Totals	120 to 250	95 to 195

Appendix B deals with the radiations that have been added by nuclear bomb tests and with the nuclear processes that produce them.

Fission and Fusion

Half a century ago Albert Einstein realized that matter could be converted to energy with an enormous yield, measured by the mass, m, times the square of the velocity of light, c^2. This energy conversion, described by the "Einstein equation," $E = mc^2$, is the basis of the great explosive force of the fission and fusion bombs and also of the peaceful uses of nuclear energy.

The nucleus of the atom is composed of tightly bound neutrons and protons (called nucleons). The "nuclear force" that holds these particles together is still not completely understood; but it is a very powerful force, and the particles are so tightly bound that enormous energy must be supplied from the outside to break them apart.

As an example let us consider the nucleus of heavy hydrogen, consisting of a proton and a neutron. The proton has a mass of 1.67239×10^{-24} of a gram, and the neutron, 1.67470×10^{-24} of a gram. By simple addition we would expect this nucleus (the deuteron) to have a mass of 3.34709×10^{-24} of a gram. But when accurately measured, the mass of the deuteron turns out to be 3.34314×10^{-24} of a gram. The 0.00395×10^{-24} difference in mass has been converted into the "binding energy" of the combination.

It is a fundamental law of nature that her processes always

develop in such a way as to minimize energy (*e.g.*, water always runs downhill). The neutron and proton convert mass to energy when they come together, and this energy is radiated away as a gamma ray of about two million electron volts. The particles are thus in a lower energy state as the deuteron than as separate particles. We can think of the deuteron combination as in an "energy well" (see Figure 23).

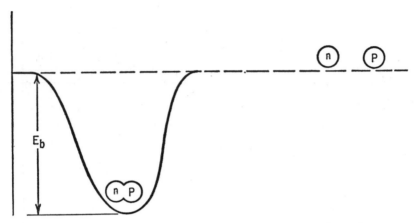

FIG. 23. Energy well of a deuteron in the lowest energy state. E_b is the binding energy.

To raise the bound particles from this well—in other words, to separate the neutron and the proton—we must provide an amount of energy sufficient to boost them over the top, much as we would have to kick a soccer ball to give it enough energy to rise to a certain height. This energy, E_b, is what is called the binding energy.

When two neutrons and two protons combine to form a helium nucleus, or alpha particle, the loss of mass is greater than in the case of the deuteron, so the alpha particle is even more tightly bound, *i.e.*, lies in a much deeper energy well.

We could repeat this process for all the stable elements and we would find that the mass of the bound nucleus is always less than the combined mass of the component neutrons and protons. However, the mass difference per particle, or binding energy, is not the same for all nuclei. The binding energy is greatest in the nuclei of medium weight and is less strong in both the very light and the very heavy elements (see Figure 24). This provides a clue to ways in which the nucleus can be made to give up its energy. We can see two ways.

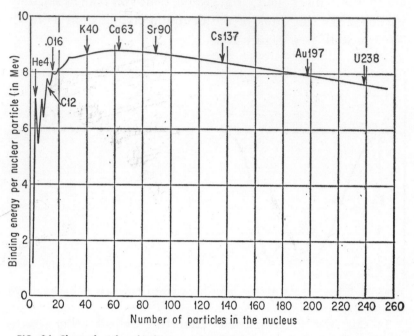

FIG. 24. Chart of nuclear binding energies of the elements in the Periodic Table. The nuclei indicated by symbols are helium 4, carbon 12, oxygen 16, potassium 40, copper 63, strontium 90, cesium 137, gold 197, and uranium 238.

Fission

First, if we can somehow split a heavy nucleus, such as uranium 238, into two medium-weight nuclei, the mass difference per particle will increase and energy will be released. The increase in mass difference amounts to about one million electron volts of energy per particle, or better than 200 million electron volts in all. This process, called "fission," also releases neutrons.

Two problems had to be solved to make the fission reaction a practical source of power: (1) splitting the nucleus, and (2) making this reaction self-sustaining. The first was not difficult: in fact, the uranium nucleus occasionally fissions spontaneously, because of its inherent instability. We can enhance this instability and speed up fissions in a sample of uranium by bombarding it with energetic particles. The easiest way is to use neutrons, for their lack of electrical charge enables them to enter the nucleus readily, whereas a charged particle has to overcome the repulsive force field of the uranium nucleus's 92 protons. Fast neutrons (of a few million electron volts energy) can cause any of the heavy elements to undergo fission.

The uranium nucleus splits in various ways, yielding pieces of different size. The most common division is into a pair of nuclei with, respectively, 90 and 140 nucleons—e.g., isotopes of strontium and xenon. But more than 100 other fission fragments have been identified and practically all of them are radioactive and decay into daughter nuclei, so that the total number of "fission products" is very large—in the neighborhood of 200.

Two single themselves out for special notice, because of their abundance and their long life, which make them particularly important in fallout. One is strontium 90, with a half-life of 28 years. In its decay, it emits an electron with an energy ranging up to more than half a million electron volts. Its daughter is yttrium 90, which after a half-life of only 64 hours emits an electron of up to 2.3 million electron volts. Thus strontium 90 can be thought of as emitting two high-speed electrons, or shots of radiation, in succession.

The second important fission product is cesium 137, with a half-life of 30 years. It emits a gamma ray of nearly three quarters of a million electron volts and an electron of about half a million electron volts. Its daughter, barium 137, emits a gamma ray of equal energy after a half-life of 2.6 minutes.

The second problem in exploiting fission—how to arrange a self-sustaining reaction—took a great deal longer to solve but also had a fairly straightforward solution. Each fission on the average releases two or more neutrons. Fortunately they do not have enough energy to cause uranium 238 to fission; if they

did, any sizable concentration of uranium in nature would become an atomic bomb triggerable by a wandering cosmic ray.
But the fission-released neutrons can split uranium 235, the
rarer isotope, which is present in natural uranium in the ratio
of one atom to every 140 atoms of uranium 238. In a mass of
U-235, the neutrons from fissions can spark a self-sustaining
chain reaction. By laborious physical methods, U-235 can be
separated from U-238. It turned out also that another fissionable
fuel could be obtained somewhat more cheaply. This is plutonium 239, which, like uranium 235, has an odd number of
neutrons and is able to bind an incoming neutron tightly
enough to release the energy needed for fission. Plutonium has
so short a half-life in geological terms (24,000 years) that it
has disappeared in nature, but it can be manufactured from
uranium 238 by adding a neutron to the latter. Of course this
means that the chain reaction in uranium must be controlled
and slowed down, instead of being allowed to roar on to an explosion as in the bomb. The story of how Enrico Fermi and his
co-workers at the University of Chicago first achieved a controlled chain reaction by introducing a "moderator" (graphite)
is now familiar to everyone. The plutonium plants are large
reactors of precisely that type.

Fusion

We noted that there are two ways to get a net yield of energy
out of the nucleus. The second is the precise opposite of the
first: instead of splitting, or fissioning, nuclei, one fuses them
together. The combination of light nuclei, like the splitting of
heavy ones, again increases the mass difference per particle, and
so releases energy. The fusion reaction, however, calls for a large
initial outlay of energy. In a sense the fusion reaction is like an
ordinary burning process. To start the fire we have to heat the
fuel to its ignition temperature. In the case of nuclear fusion
the "ignition temperature" is extremely high, because the repul-

sive forces between nuclei are so strong that it takes enormous energy to bring them together closely enough to fuse. The reluctant nuclei have to be pushed up an electrical hill, so to speak. The height of this hill for deuterons is about 15,000 electron volts. This is not a very impressive energy as conventional energies go: any dentist's X-ray machine can accelerate electrons to 15,000 volts. But to raise many of the deuterons in a sample of deuterium gas to the velocity they would have if accelerated through 15,000 electron volts would require a temperature of about ten million degrees, which is somewhere near the temperature in the interior of the sun. And to make the fusion reaction self-sustaining, the temperature must approach 100 million degrees.

There are only two ways man has been able to achieve energies sufficient to make nuclei fuse. One is by exploding a fission bomb, which creates the necessary heat. The other is by accelerating particles in a cyclotron so that they fuse with a few nuclei in a target. The cyclotron, allowing us to study the fusion reaction on a submicroscopic scale, has told us a good deal about what happens.

Deuterons fuse somewhat more easily than protons (the nuclei of ordinary hydrogen), and so they make a better fuel. When two deuterons are brought very close together, strong forces of attraction take over, with the result that one deuteron seizes a particle from the other—either its proton or its neutron. If the captured particle is the proton, the fused nucleus has two protons and a neutron, which is helium 3, the rare isotope of helium; if one deuteron captures the other's neutron, the new nucleus, with one proton and two neutrons, is tritium, a hydrogen isotope (see Figure 25). The escaping neutron in the first case carries an energy of three million electron volts; the proton in the second case, four million electron volts. So from having rolled the two deuterons up the 15,000-electron-volt hill (see Figure 26), we harvest a yield of three or four million electron volts!

Other fusion combinations are possible. A deuteron can com-

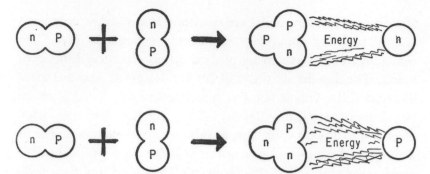

FIG. 25. The two fusion reactions of deuterons. At the top, a deuteron fuses with a proton, releasing a neutron and energy; at the bottom, a deuteron fuses with a neutron, with release of a proton and energy.

bine with the nucleus of either helium 3 or tritium with an even more impressive yield of energy—about 18 million electron volts. Tritium would be an ideal fusion fuel if it could be produced in sufficient quantity. It can be made by bombarding lithium 6 with neutrons (see Figure 27). When the lithium nucleus (three protons, three neutrons) captures a neutron, it splits into tritium

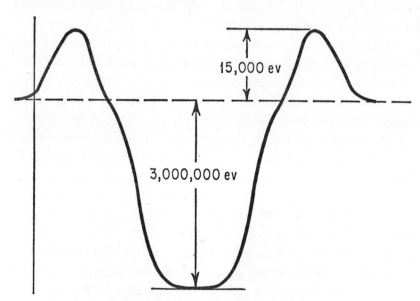

FIG. 26. Deuterons' energy well. When boosted over the 15,000-electron-volt hill, they fuse and yield three million electron volts.

and helium 4 (ordinary helium), with an energy yield of 4.8 million electron volts.

The results of the fission and fusion reactions differ in two very important respects. First, fusion produces a great many excess neutrons, which may induce radioactivity in the surroundings and have such high energies that they can fission uranium 238, thus making a superbomb possible (see Chapter 1). Secondly, the fusion reaction itself is a "clean" reaction, because its only radioactive product (in contrast to the products of fission) is tritium, which emits comparatively weak radiation, has a fairly short half-life (12 years), and becomes so diluted in the world's waters that it is not a fallout hazard.

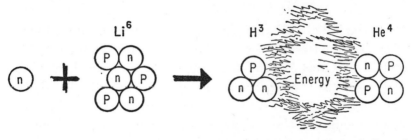

FIG. 27. Fission of lithium 6 by a neutron. The unstable combination splits into hydrogen 3 and helium 4, releasing 4.8 million electron volts of energy.

The complete "burning" of the deuterons and their products (tritium and helium 3) in a fusion cycle would produce about seven million electron volts per deuteron. This corresponds to 43 million kilowatt-hours per pound of deuterium. In comparison, gasoline, a highly refined chemical fuel, produces six kilowatt-hours per pound. Although in nature there is only one molecule containing deuterium for every 6,700 ordinary water molecules, the deuterium in one gallon of ordinary water has an energy content equal to that in 350 gallons of gasoline. Thus the potential energy reserve in the oceans is virtually inexhaustible.

APPENDIX C

List of Nuclear
Explosions

Up to the fall of 1958 there had been 203 announced explosions
of nuclear devices—129 by the United States, 53 by the U.S.S.R.,
and 21 by Great Britain. The sites and actual numbers of explosions in the U.S.S.R. are not known precisely; the listed tests
are those reported by the Soviet government and/or by United
States monitors. The complete list of known detonations by
the three nations follows:

United States

July 16, 1945—First atomic bomb test, "Trinity,"
     Alamogordo, N.M.
August 6, 1945—Hiroshima bomb
August 9, 1945—Nagasaki bomb
Summer of 1946—"Crossroads" tests (2), Bikini Atoll
Spring of 1948—"Sandstone" tests (3), Eniwetok Proving Ground
Winter of 1951—"Ranger" tests (5), Nevada Test Site
Spring of 1951—"Greenhouse" tests (4), Eniwetok
Fall of 1951—"Buster-Jangle" tests (7), Nevada
Spring of 1952—"Tumbler-Snapper" tests (8), Nevada
Fall of 1952—"Ivy" tests (2), Eniwetok

Spring of 1953—"Upshot-Knothole" tests (11), Nevada
Spring of 1954—"Castle" tests (6), Eniwetok
Spring of 1955—"Teapot" tests (14), Nevada
Spring of 1955—"Wigwam" test (1), Pacific Ocean
Spring-Summer of 1956—"Redwing" tests (4), Eniwetok
Spring-Summer of 1957—"Plumb-bob" tests (24), Nevada
Spring-Summer of 1958—"Hardtack" series, first phase (16), Eniwetok
Fall of 1958—"Hardtack" series, second phase (19), Nevada

U.S.S.R.

September 23, 1949—First Soviet nuclear explosion
October, 1951—Two known tests
August, 1953—Series of tests, two known explosions, one thermonuclear
October 26, 1954—"Part of a series"
August 4, 1955—One explosion
September 24, 1955—"Part of a series"
November, 1955—"Part of a series," two explosions, one "in megaton range"
March-April, 1956—"Part of a series," two explosions
August-September, 1956—"Part of a series," four explosions
November 17, 1956—One explosion
January 19, 1957—"Part of a series"
March-April, 1957—"Part of a series," six explosions
August-October, 1957—"Part of a series," five explosions
December 28, 1957—One explosion
February-March, 1958—Nine explosions
September-November, 1958—Sixteen explosions

Great Britain

October 3, 1952—First British explosion, Monte Bello Islands
October, 1953—Two explosions, Woomera

May-June, 1956—Two explosions, Monte Bello Islands
September-October, 1956—Four explosions, Marelinga
May-June, 1957—Three explosions, Christmas Island
September-October, 1957—Three explosions, Marelinga
November 8, 1957—One explosion, Christmas Island
April 28, 1958—One explosion, Christmas Island
August-September, 1958—Four explosions

In the 203 explosions the total energy yield from fission (*i.e.*, not including fusion energy) was an estimated 91,460,000 tons. This estimate is based on the assumption that the Soviet thermonuclear tests consisted on the average of 50 per cent fission and 50 per cent fusion, as did the United States and British tests. Lumping together the fission detonations by the three nations, the proportions exploded in the air, on the ground, and at the sea surface are given in the following table:

FISSION YIELD IN KILOTONS

	Air Bursts	Ground Surface Bursts	Water Surface Bursts
1945–1951	190	550	20
1952–1954	1,000	15,000	22,000
1955–1956	5,600	1,500	6,000
1957–1958	31,000	4,400	4,600

Casualties in a Nuclear Attack

In the Congressional "nuclear war hearings" of 1959, experts presented estimates of the casualties that would result from a 3,000-megaton attack on the United States. It was assumed that each of the largest metropolitan areas would be hit by two 10-megaton bombs, and the smaller centers by correspondingly smaller weapons. The estimated casualties in the attacked areas are given, city by city, in the following table (the location in each case includes the entire metropolitan area):

Target Area and Weapons	Population	Number Killed First Day	Fatally Injured	Injured Non-fatally
Two 10-megaton weapons each				
Boston	2,875,000	1,052,000	1,084,000	467,000
Chicago	5,498,000	545,000	447,000	648,000
Detroit	3,017,000	820,000	593,000	557,000
Los Angeles	4,367,000	698,000	2,136,000	814,000
New York	12,904,000	3,464,000	2,634,000	2,278,000
Philadelphia	3,671,000	1,309,000	989,000	777,000
One 10- and one 8-megaton weapon each				
Baltimore	1,338,000	591,000	466,000	174,000
Cleveland	1,466,000	394,000	298,000	316,000
Pittsburgh	2,214,000	597,000	659,000	43,000
St. Louis	1,292,000	563,000	370,000	161,000
San Francisco	2,241,000	734,000	769,000	301,000
Washington, D.C.	1.465,000	579,000	433,000	228,000

Target Area and Weapons	Population	Number Killed First Day	Fatally Injured	Injured Non-fatally
One 10-megaton weapon each				
Atlanta	672,000	155,000	206,000	160,000
Buffalo	1,089,000	253,000	140,000	158,000
Cincinnati	904,000	461,000	261,000	93,000
Dallas	614,000	130,000	314,000	124,000
Houston	807,000	81,000	57,000	114,000
Kansas City	814,000	265,000	230,000	144,000
Milwaukee	872,000	151,000	112,000	189,000
Minneapolis	1,117,000	201,000	92,000	97,000
New Orleans	685,000	319,000	226,000	74,000
Portland	705,000	156,000	103,000	131,000
Providence	682,000	210,000	263,000	144,000
Seattle	732,000	168,000	99,000	126,000
One 8-megaton weapon each				
Albany	514,000	69,000	51,000	63,000
Birmingham	559,000	159,000	137,000	86,000
Columbus	504,000	245,000	134,000	54,000
Dayton	458,000	200,000	119,000	58,000
Denver	564,000	138,000	144,000	118,000
Indianapolis	552,000	137,000	88,000	209,000
Louisville	577,000	264,000	156,000	59,000
Memphis	482,000	76,000	51,000	97,000
Norfolk	446,000	180,000	117,000	59,000
Rochester	488,000	212,000	107,000	59,000
San Diego	557,000	58,000	202,000	126,000
Youngstown	529,000	121,000	189,000	76,000
One 3- and one 2-megaton weapon each				
Akron	410,000	162,000	104,000	66,000
Allentown	436,000	45,000	79,000	117,000
Fort Worth	361,000	73,000	189,000	74,000
Hartford (New Britain)	539,000	124,000	110,000	119,000
Springfield-Holyoke	456,000	157,000	100,000	72,000
Toledo	396,000	107,000	74,000	75,000
Wilkes-Barre	393,000	51,000	48,000	63,000
One 3-megaton weapon each				
Bridgeport	504,000	105,000	84,000	54,000
Canton	283,000	84,000	59,000	42,000
Chattanooga	246,000	85,000	77,000	29,000
Davenport	234,000	73,000	53,000	53,000
Erie	219,000	54,000	42,000	42,000
Flint	271,000	77,000	46,000	39,000
Grand Rapids	287,000	124,000	66,000	21,000
Knoxville	337,000	112,000	106,000	38,000
Lancaster	235,000	54,000	51,000	49,000

Target Area and Weapons	Population	Number Killed First Day	Fatally Injured	Injured Non-fatally
One 3-megaton weapon each (*Continued*)				
New Haven (Waterbury)	546,000	192,000	138,000	95,000
Peoria	250,000	84,000	54,000	28,000
Reading	256,000	72,000	66,000	60,000
South Bend	205,000	84,000	53,000	34,000
Syracuse	342,000	89,000	68,000	73,000
Trenton	230,000	41,000	80,000	97,000
Utica-Rome	284,000	107,000	60,000	2,000
Wheeling	355,000	59,000	58,000	46,000
Wichita	222,000	78,000	75,000	38,000
Wilmington	269,000	77,000	76,000	67,000
Worcester	547,000	128,000	151,000	97,000
One 1-megaton weapon each				
Binghamton	185,000	58,000	32,000	17,000
Evansville	161,000	60,000	34,000	23,000
Fort Wayne	184,000	69,000	41,000	23,000
Greensboro	191,000	28,000	19,000	32,000
New Britain (included with Hartford)				
Rockford	152,000	42,000	25,000	25,000
Waterbury (included with New Haven)				
York	203,000	46,000	31,000	17,000
Total Within Target Areas	68,460,000	18,556,000	16,825,000	11,009,000
Total Outside Target Areas	82,239,000	1,095,000	5,354,000	6,182,000
Grand Total	150,699,000	19,651,000	22,179,000	17,191,000

Glossary

activity:—The activity of a radioactive material is a measure of the number of atoms that disintegrate per unit time. It is usually measured in curies.

alpha particle:—A particle often emitted by heavy radioactive nuclei. It consists of two protons and two neutrons and ionizes heavily due to its relatively large charge and mass. The energy is measured in millions of electron volts.

artificial radioactivity:—The radioactivity produced by adding or subtracting neutrons or protons from the nucleus or in some way altering the constitution of a nucleus. Most of the artificially radioactive elements have short physical half-lives.

atom:—The atom is the smallest chemical unit and consists of an electron cloud of radius on the order of 10^{-8} cm. around a positively charged nucleus of radius about 10^{-12} cm. The atom of a given element is identified by its atomic number, *i.e.*, the number of electrons about the nucleus.

atomic bomb:—The nuclear weapon that derives its energy from the fission reaction. Sizes range from the equivalent of a few thousand tons of TNT to several hundred thousand.

atomic number:—The number of electrons in the atom and therefore the number of protons in the nucleus. The elements are characterized by their atomic number and are ordered by it in the Periodic Table, there being about 102 elements in all.

background:—A term used to describe the natural radiation of the earth and its atmosphere. It consists of cosmic radiation and radioactivity in the earth, air, and water.

beta particle:—A high-speed electron emitted by nuclei which are neutron-rich. As electrons are very light, even with only a few hundred kilovolts of energy they move at speeds near that of light, 3×10^{10} cm/sec. They therefore ionize slightly in comparison to protons or alpha particles of the same energy.

biological half-life:—The biological half-life of a radioactive element is the time needed to reduce the number of atoms of this material in the body to one half their initial value, the reduction being by biological processes and not by radioactive decay.

bone marrow:—The soft tissue that constitutes the central filling of many bones and is responsible for the production of blood corpuscles.

BTU, British Thermal Unit:—The amount of energy required to raise the temperature of one pound of water 1° Fahrenheit.

calcium:—The element with atomic number 20. An important constituent of bone and of most living systems.

carbon 14:—A radioactive isotope of carbon formed in the atmosphere by neutron bombardment of nitrogen. Carbon 14 emits a beta particle of maximum energy 0.16 Mev and has a half-life of 5,600 years.

carcinoma:—Malignant tumors derived from the outer skin, the lining of the body cavities, and certain glands.

cesium 137:—A radioactive isotope of cesium, the element of atomic number 55. It emits a .66 Mev gamma ray and a beta particle, thus decaying to barium 137, which also emits a .66 Mev gamma. Cesium 137 has a half-life of 30 years.

chromosome:—An important constituent of all cells, the chromosome is a thread-like structure which contains the genes, the basic heredity-determining units. The number of chromosomes per cell varies greatly from organism to organism; man has 46.

cosmic rays:—High-energy particles which bombard the earth from outer space. The particles hitting the top of the atmosphere are mostly protons, but in the collisions with air nuclei, other forms of radiation are produced, with a wide range of energies and penetrating power.

critical mass:—The critical mass is that amount of a fissionable material which will sustain a chain reaction. The mass must be of a size, shape, density, and purity so that more neutrons are produced by fission events than are lost in non-fissioning events.

curie:—The curie is a measure of the activity or strength of a sample of radioactive material. It is expressed in terms of particles emitted per second, or disintegrations per second. One curie of a radioactive material emits 3.70×10^{10} particles per second. One gram of radium has an activity of one curie.

daughter product:—The nucleus left when a radioactive nucleus emits a particle. In many cases the daughter product is also radioactive.

decay:—Synonymous with disintegration. The spontaneous emission of a particle from a radioactive nucleus.

deuterium:—The name for the isotope of hydrogen which has a neutron and proton in its nucleus. Deuterium oxide, D_2O, is heavy water. Deuterium is present in the ratio 1/6700 in ordinary hydrogen.

dose:—The dose or exposure is the energy transmitted to the irradiated material. See rad, rem, rep, roentgen.

electron:—A fundamental particle with negative charge. Electrons take up most of the volume of the atom but little of the mass. The mass of the electron is 9.11×10^{-28} gm.

electron volt:—The energy gained by an electron being accelerated through a potential difference of one volt. One electron volt is the equivalent of 4.5×10^{-26} kilowatt-hour or 1.6×10^{-22} BTU. Thus 6.3×10^{21} electron volts of energy would be needed to raise one pound of water 1° Fahrenheit.

erg:—A unit of energy, equivalent to 6.3×10^{11} electron volts. One erg is equal to about 10^{-10} BTU or 2.8×10^{-14} kilowatt-hour.

fallout:—The name given to the radioactive debris from nuclear weapons.

fission:—The nuclear process in which a nucleus splits in two and releases energy. It is a process characteristic of the heavy elements, uranium, plutonium, thorium, etc. This process provides the energy for the atomic bomb and nuclear reactors.

fusion:—The nuclear process in which two light nuclei join together to form a heavier one. It occurs most readily with hydrogen and its isotopes. This process provides the energy for the hydrogen bomb.

gamma ray:—A penetrating radiation emitted by a radioactive nucleus. It is of the same general nature as X-rays and ordinary light, though more energetic. Its energy is usually a few Mev. Gamma rays of this energy can penetrate considerable thicknesses of matter.

geiger counter:—A device used to detect radiation by collecting and observing the pulse of ions created in an enclosed sample of gas by the passage of energetic particles.

genes:—The basic hereditary units which singly or in combination determine heritable character. The genes are located at certain specific points along the chromosome.

gonads:—The male and female glands in which the reproductive cells are formed, *i.e.*, the testes and ovaries.

gram:—A unit of mass commonly used in scientific work. It is very nearly the mass of one cubic centimeter of water, or about one thousandth of a quart.

half-life:—The physical half-life of a radioactive nucleus is the time during which it has a 50:50 chance of disintegrating. Given a collection of nuclei of the same species, the half-life is the time during which half of them will undergo disintegration and change into the daughter product.

heavy water:—Water in which hydrogen has been replaced by its heavier isotope deuterium. It is called deuterium oxide.

hydrogen bomb:—A bomb in which all or part of the energy derives from the fusion process. The energy ranges from hundreds of thousands to millions of tons of TNT-equivalent.

ICRP:—The International Commission on Radiological Protection. An international body of radiologists which recommends tolerance levels, safety practices, etc.

ion:—The positively charged atom from which an electron has been separated.

ionization:—The process in which an electron is separated from a neutral atom by the force of attraction or repulsion exerted on it by a passing charged particle.

isotope:—Isotopes are nuclei having the same number of protons *i.e.,* the same atomic number, but differing in the number of neutrons, *i.e.,* having different atomic weights. Isotopes of an element are chemically identical but possess quite dissimilar nuclear properties.

kilo:—A prefix meaning one thousand. Thus a kilo-electron volt (kev) is 1,000 electron volts, a kiloton is 1,000 tons.

kiloton:—A measure of nuclear weapon energy. A one-kiloton weapon releases the same amount of energy as would 1,000 tons of TNT.

LD-50:—The radiation exposure that will kill 50 per cent of the irradiated organisms. The LD-50 for man is about 500 rads.

leukemia:—A malignant blood disease in which the white blood cells are produced to excess.

Maximum Permissible Concentration (MPC):—The maximum concentration of a radioactive isotope considered safe for any individual. The concept is applied to industry or laboratory situations, and the MPC for the population is usually taken to be one tenth of the occupational MPC.

mega:—A prefix meaning million (10^6); thus a megacurie is a million curies.

Mev:—Million electron volts. See electron volts.

micro:—A prefix meaning one millionth; thus a microcurie is one millionth of a curie.

micromicro:—A prefix meaning a millionth of a millionth (10^{-12}).

milli:—A prefix meaning one thousandth; thus one milliroentgen is one thousandth of a roentgen.

mutation:—A transformation of the gene which alters its heritable character. Mutations may be induced by radiation.

neutron:—Along with the proton a basic building block of the nucleus. The neutron has about the same mass as the proton but is uncharged. Free neutrons decay to protons plus beta particles with a half-life of 12 minutes.

nuclear reactor:—A device in which a controlled chain reaction takes place in fissionable material. The control is usually through rods of neutron-absorbing materials.

nucleon:—A proton or a neutron.

nucleus:—The solid core of the atom, of the order of 10^{-12} cm. in radius. It consists of neutrons and protons, is positively charged, and contains almost all the mass of the atom.

nuclide:—A nuclear species, a specific isotope.

plutonium:—One of the very heavy elements, atomic number 94. Plutonium 239 is used as a fissionable material in nuclear weapons.

positron:—A positive particle emitted by proton-rich nuclei. It has the same mass as the electron and a charge equal in magnitude but positive.

potassium 40:—A radioactive isotope which emits a 1.3 Mev beta particle and gamma rays. It has a half-life of 1.3×10^9 years.

rad:—A unit of radiation exposure, or absorbed dose. It is a measure of the energy imparted to a piece of irradiated material and is defined as 100 ergs per gram. It is the unit recommended by the International Commission on **Radiological Units**.

radioactivity:—The unstable condition of a nuclear species which causes it to spontaneously emit energetic particles.

Relative Biological Effectiveness (RBE):—The ratio of the gamma or X-ray exposure to the exposure of some other radiation needed to produce the same biological effect. For beta and gamma particles, the RBE is 1; for alphas, 20; for protons, 10.

rem (roentgen equivalent man):—The most common unit of radiation exposure, or dose. It is that quantity of ionizing radiation which produces, when absorbed by man, an effect equivalent to the absorption of one roentgen of X-rays or gamma radiation. The dose in rem is obtained by multiplying the dose in rads by the appropriate RBE.

rep (roentgen equivalent physical):—A measure of absorbed radiation. The amount of ionizing radiation which will result in the absorption of 83 ergs in one gram of tissue. (Some authorities use 93 ergs.)

roentgen:—The standard measure of X-ray exposure, usually abbreviated r. It is that exposure which in 0.001293 gm. of air will produce ions carrying a total of one electrostatic unit of charge, *i.e.*, about 10^9 electrons and a like number of positive ions. This energy absorption amounts to about 88 ergs per gram.

somatic:—Pertaining to all tissues other than the reproductive cells. Somatic effects are limited to the irradiated organism itself and do not carry over to succeeding generations.

stratosphere:—The portion of the atmosphere above the troposphere. In this region the temperature changes but little with altitude, and clouds of water vapor never form.

strontium:—The element of atomic number 38. Strontium 90, one of its radioactive isotopes, emits a 0.61 Mev beta particle and has a half-life of 28 years.

strontium unit:—A measure of the concentration of strontium 90 in food and in the body (*i.e.*, in bone). The concentration is measured as the ratio of strontium to calcium, the chemical cousin with which strontium becomes mixed in soil and living tissue. One strontium unit is one micromicrocurie of strontium 90 per gram of calcium.

tritium:—A radioactive isotope of hydrogen, with two neutrons and a proton in its nucleus. Tritium emits a beta particle with a maximum energy of 18,000 electron volts and has a half-life of 12.3 years.

tropopause:—The imaginary boundary between the stratosphere and the troposphere. In middle latitudes its height is about 30,000 to 40,000 feet; in the tropics it is 50,000 to 60,000 feet above the earth's surface. The height depends somewhat on the season.

troposphere:—The lower part of the earth's atmosphere, containing our weather—clouds, rain, mist, etc.

uranium:—The element of atomic number 92. The common isotope, uranium 238, emits an alpha particle of 4.2 Mev; it has a half-life of 4.5×10^9 years. Natural uranium is 99.3 per cent uranium 238 and 0.7 per cent uranium 235.

X-rays:—Artificially produced radiation similar to gamma rays. Its penetrating power depends on the energy of the rays, which ranges from tens of thousands to hundreds of thousands of electron volts.

Index